# A. J. Wentworth, B.A.

H. F. Ellis

# A. J. Wentworth, B.A.

*Containing* THE PAPERS OF A. J. WENTWORTH, B.A.
*and* THE PAPERS OF A. J. WENTWORTH, B.A. (RET'D)

Weidenfeld and Nicolson
London

The material in this book is adapted from articles which originally appeared in *Punch*

Subsequently published in two separate books as
THE PAPERS OF A. J. WENTWORTH, B.A.
by Evans Brothers, 1949, and
A. J. WENTWORTH, B.A. (RET'D)
by Geoffrey Bles, 1962

Published in Penguin Books 1964

Published by George Weidenfeld and Nicolson Limited
91 Clapham High Street, London sw4

ISBN 0 297 77761 0

Printed in Great Britain by
REDWOOD BURN LIMITED
Trowbridge & Esher

# Contents

# Introduction

Attempts to persuade my old friend Arthur James Wentworth to allow me to give to the public certain hitherto unrecorded episodes in his not unremarkable career – a visit to the United States, for instance, and the story of his acquittal on a charge of driving a motor-mower without due care and attention – have so far proved unsuccessful. 'Plenty of time, plenty of time,' he is apt to say; 'these decisions must not be rushed.' Now in his eighty-third year (assuming, that is, that we are to take as correct an impertinent observation made by the boy Atkins as long ago as July 1939), though he looks younger, Mr Wentworth seems oblivious of the passage of the years. It is not for me to remind him that the Great Reaper, unlike the boys of Set IIIA at Burgrove cannot be kept indefinitely at bay by a dismissive glance.

He has, however, consented to the republication of his papers or (in his own phrase) 'occasional jottings', which first saw the light in book form at intervals between 1949 and 1962. A whole new generation of schoolmasters has grasped the chalk since those distant days and, from all Mr Wentworth hears and reads, is sadly in need of such guidance as an experienced old hand can give. In particular, the monstrous misconception that in no circumstances is a master justified in throwing books etc. at his boys – the heresy that originally decided him to give the benefit of his own experience to the profession – has if anything grown more widespread since his retirement. On occasion, after reading of some teacher reprimanded or even dismissed by what he calls a 'set of ignorant busybodies' for nothing more than a straightforward disciplinary swipe, Mr Wentworth expresses himself with unaccustomed violence. 'God bless my soul!' he has been heard to say.

The original publication of the first part of the present book, for which I endeavoured to select, at his request, only such material as threw light on the forces militating against the composure and, indeed, the sanity of assistant masters, led to some misguided criticism of his character and general outlook on life. In particular he resented the suggestion, made by several correspondents, that he was 'just a typical narrow-minded schoolmaster', with no ideas or interests beyond time-tables, square brackets and Matron's concern for the boys' socks. Eventually, after his retirement, he felt it his duty, if only in fairness to his profession, to counter these damaging misconceptions, and accordingly sent me a further instalment of personal jottings, cuttings from local papers, theatre-ticket stubs, travel literature and, for some reason, a bulb catalogue with 'Narrow-minded, my foot!' scrawled across the cover. 'Do what you like with these,' he wrote, 'as long as you give a fair picture of my life and philosophy of living, both here at Fenport and on my, I think I may claim, fairly extensive travels. I make no explicit defence or apologia. It appears to me that a simple, straightforward account of my life, as I live it in retirement from day to day, should suffice to show that, for variety and breadth of interests, civic sense, tolerance and a readiness to meet and mingle with all sorts and conditions of men and (up to a point of course) women, a retired schoolmaster can hold a candle to any Tom, Dick or Harry.'

Here then, with the addition of a couple of notes kindly sent me by his colleague Mr Gilbert which clear up one or two points left in some obscurity by my old friend, is the first-hand record of A. J. Wentworth at work and play (and, indeed, at war) – a record upon which he is content, he tells me, to let his reputation stand or fall before the bar of public opinion. He himself, I ought to add, remains in no doubt whatever of the verdict.

H. F. ELLIS

*Kingston St Mary, Somerset 1979*

The Papers of
A. J. Wentworth, B.A.

# Statement of
# Arthur James Wentworth, B.A.

My name is Arthur James Wentworth, I am unmarried and I am by profession an assistant master at Burgrove Preparatory School, Wilminster. The Headmaster is the Reverend Gregory Saunders, M.A. He is known to the boys as the Squid – not necessarily, I think, a term of opprobrium. He is a classical scholar of moderate attainments, a generous employer and much given to the use of the expression, 'The School must come first, Wentworth.' I attach no particular meaning to this remark.

At 11.15 on the morning of Saturday 8 July, I entered Classroom 4 for the purpose of instructing Set IIIA in Algebra. There were present Anderson, Atkins, Clarke, Etheridge, Hillman, Hopgood II, Mason, Otterway, Sapoulos, Trench and Williamson. Heathcote, who has, I am told, a boil, was absent. It should be explained that though I have given these names in the alphabetical order in which they appear in the school list, that is not the order in which the boys were sitting on this occasion. It is the custom at Burgrove for boys to sit according to their position in the previous week's mark-lists. Thus in the front row were seated Etheridge, a most promising mathematician, Hillman, Mason, Otterway and Clarke. Hopgood II, the boy whom I am now accused of assaulting, was in the middle of the second row. The third and last row was shared by Sapoulos, a Greek, and Atkins, a cretin. I do not think these facts have any bearing on anything that is to follow, but I give them for the sake of completeness.

'This morning,' I remarked, taking up my *Hall and Knight*, 'we will do problems,' and I told them at once that if there was any more of that groaning they would do nothing but problems for the next month. It is my experience, as an assistant master of some years' standing, that if groaning is not checked immediately it may swell to enormous proportions. I make it my business to stamp on it.

Mason, a fair-haired boy with glasses, remarked when the groaning had died down that it would not be possible to do problems for the next month, and on being asked why not, replied that there were only three weeks more of term. This was true, and I decided to make no reply. He then asked if he could have a mark for that. I said, 'No, Mason, you may not,' and, taking up my book and a piece of chalk, read out, 'I am just half as old as my father and in twenty years I shall be five years older than he was twenty years ago. How old am I?' Atkins promptly replied, 'Forty-two.' I inquired of him how, unless he was gifted with supernatural powers, he imagined he could produce the answer without troubling to do any working-out. He said, 'I saw it in the *Schools Year-book*.' This stupid reply caused a great deal of laughter, which I suppressed.

I should have spoken sharply to Atkins, but at this moment I noticed that his neighbour Sapoulos, the Greek boy, appeared to be eating toffee, a practice which is forbidden at Burgrove during school hours. I ordered him to stand up. 'Sapoulos,' I said, 'you are not perhaps quite used yet to our English ways, and I shall not punish you this time for your disobedience; but please understand that I will not have eating in my class. You did not come here to eat but to learn. If you try hard and pay attention, I do not altogether despair of teaching you something, but if you do not wish to learn I cannot help you. You might as well go back to your own country.' Mason, without being given permission to speak, cried excitedly, 'He can't, sir. Didn't you know? His father was chased out of Greece in a revolution or something. A big man with a black beard chased him for three miles and he had to escape in a small boat. It's true, sir. You ask him. Sapoulos got hit on the knee with a brick, didn't you, Sappy? And his grandmother – at least I think it was his grandmother – '

'That will do, Mason,' I said. 'Who threw that?'

I am not, I hope, a martinet, but I will not tolerate the

throwing of paper darts, or other missiles in my algebra set. Some of the boys make small pellets out of their blotting-paper and flick them with their garters. This sort of thing has to be put down with a firm hand or work becomes impossible. I accordingly warned the boy responsible that another offence would mean an imposition. He had the impertinence to ask what sort of an imposition. I said that it would be a pretty stiff imposition, and if he wished to know more exact details he had only to throw another dart to find out. He thereupon threw another dart.

I confess that at this I lost patience and threatened to keep the whole set in during the afternoon if I had any more trouble. The lesson then proceeded.

It was not until I had completed my working out of the problem on the board that I realized I had worked on the assumption – of course ridiculous – that I was *twice* my father's age instead of *half*. This gave the false figure of minus 90 for my own age. Some boy said, 'Crikey!' I at once whipped round and demanded to know who had spoken. Otterway suggested that it might have been Hopgood II talking in his sleep. I was about to reprimand Otterway for impertinence when I realized that Hopgood actually was asleep and had in fact, according to Williamson, been asleep since the beginning of the period. Mason said, 'He hasn't missed much, anyway.'

I then threw my *Hall and Knight*. It has been suggested that it was intended to hit Hopgood II. This is false. I never wake up sleeping boys by throwing books at them, as hundreds of old Burgrove boys will be able to testify. I intended to hit Mason, and it was by a mischance which I shall always regret that Hopgood was struck. I have had, as I told my Headmaster, a great deal to put up with from Mason, and no one who knows the boy blames me for the attempt to do him some physical violence. It is indeed an accepted maxim in the Common Room that physical violence is the only method of dealing with Mason which produces any results; to this the Headmaster some time ago added a rider that the boy be instructed to remove his spectacles before being assaulted. That I forgot to do this must be put down to the natural agitation of a mathematics master caught out in an error. But I blame myself for it.

I do not blame myself for the unfortunate stunning of Hopgood II. It was an accident. I did all I could for the boy when it was discovered (I think by Etheridge) that he had been rendered unconscious. I immediately summoned the Headmaster and we talked the matter over. We agreed that concealment was impossible that that I must give a full account of the circumstances to the police. Meanwhile the work of the school was to go on as usual; Hopgood himself would have wished it. The Headmaster added that in any case the School must come first.

I have made this statement after being duly cautioned, of my own free will and in the presence of witnesses. I have read it through three times with considerable satisfaction, and am prepared to state on oath that it is a true and full account of the circumstances leading up to the accident to Hopgood II. I wish only to add that the boy is now none the worse for the blow, and has indeed shown increased zeal for his studies since the occurrence.

(*Signed*) A. J. WENTWORTH, B.A.

*July 1939*

# Christmas Term 1938
## A Routine Week

**MONDAY**

This has been an unsatisfactory day. When I entered Classroom 4 after break I found the whole class clustered round my desk and immediately ordered them sharply to go to their places and open their books. 'Didn't you hear the bell?' I cried. 'It went two minutes ago.' Some of the boys turned round as I spoke, and I saw to my surprise that they were not IIIA, as I had expected, but the Upper Fourth, and that the Headmaster was seated at the desk correcting their exercises. I am not at all convinced that it is a wise practice to call all the boys up when one is correcting. I have tried it myself with IIIA and also with the Lower Third for English History and it does not work. The boys are inclined to jostle for places, and on one occasion IIIA pushed my desk, through over-keenness, right off its dais, with the result that a great deal of ink was spilled and Etheridge, the best worker of the lot, sprained his wrist and had to go up to Matron. But of course a headmaster has the right to do as he likes.

As soon as I realized my mistake I apologized.

'I beg your pardon, Headmaster,' I said, colouring, 'I was thinking it was Monday.'

'It *is* Monday, Mr Wentworth,' he said kindly.

There was no more to be said, so I apologized again and withdrew. I should have remembered that on Mondays I take IIIA in Room 6, since the Library, where the Headmaster ordinarily takes the Upper Fourth, is wanted by Miss Coombes for her Music now that the Music Room is used for P.T. on wet days.

On my way down the corridor to Room 6 I remembered

that I had forgotten to bring IIIA's corrected books with me and hurried back to the Common Room to get them. There I found Gilbert smoking a pipe. 'Hullo, A.J.,' he said. 'I thought you were having fun with IIIA this period.' I explained that I was looking for some exercise-books and asked if he had seen them.

'There were some old books on the table this morning,' he said; 'but I burnt those. I thought they were finished with.'

I was nearly taken in for a moment, but I know C.G. of old. 'You're pulling my leg, C.G.,' I said, doubling up my fists in pretended anger; and sure enough soon found my books at the back of my locker.

This incident delayed me still further, and in my haste to get to work I inadvertently returned to Room 4 instead of Room 6. Not wishing, naturally, to disturb the Headmaster a second time, I closed the door again as quietly as I could the moment I heard his voice conjugating the imperfect subjunctive passive of '*audio*', but even so could not help hearing him say, 'See who that was, Briggs.' I now made what proved to be the fatal mistake of running into the boot-room. This little room, in which, as the name implies, the boys keep their boots and shoes, lies on the right of a narrow passage running off the main corridor almost opposite Classroom 4, and it was natural that it should come into my mind, since the main corridor itself continues for a considerable distance on either side of Room 4 without offering concealment of any kind.

Time and again I have warned the school boot-boy not to leave the large basket, in which he collects the soiled shoes for cleaning, in the middle of the boot-room floor. It is an unnecessary obstruction, and what is more I have known boys turn it upside-down and hide under it when I have been marshalling them for a Sunday afternoon walk. But the boot-boy has, I am afraid, about as much sense as Atkins, who is easily the stupidest of my IIIA boys. I fell over, and indeed into, this basket with a considerable noise, and in so doing lost hold of my exercise-books, which flew all over the room. I was still in this ludicrous position, striving to free my gown which had caught in the wickerwork, when Briggs put his head round the door, said 'Golly!' and disappeared again, no doubt to report what he had seen to the Headmaster.

It can be imagined that I was in no mood after this to stand any nonsense from anybody, and IIIA found that they had a very different person to deal with this morning from their usual good-natured master. I kept Anderson standing up for twenty minutes and gave Mason the shock of his life by setting him fifty lines for singing. A little severity now and then does them no harm at all.

The Headmaster sent for me after lunch and was very decent about it, though obviously displeased.

'I understand, Wentworth,' he said, 'that you were seen sitting in a basket in the boot-room this morning at a time when you should have been supervising the work of one of your mathematical sets?'

I nodded my head and said eagerly that I could explain.

He said, 'No explanation is necessary. I do not make it my business, as you know, to pry into the affairs of my masters. I trust you all implicitly. But I must make it clear that I cannot allow any master to fritter away, in the boot-room or anywhere else, time which should be devoted to the instruction of my boys. That is what we are all here for – to teach.'

I told him that I was extremely sorry for what had occurred, and added that I was prepared, if he wished it, to give an undertaking never to enter the boot-room again. He replied that he did not wish it, that he hoped I had enough self-control to make such an undertaking unnecessary, and that he had no objection whatever to my going into the boot-room whenever I wished provided that neither the work of the boys nor the dignity of my position was endangered by my presence there. He then said that the School must come first, and I realized that the interview was at an end.

On my way back to the Common Room I met Mason and let him off his imposition. It had worried me to think that I might perhaps have let a momentary irritation override my sense of fair play.

TUESDAY

Every mathematics master dreads the day when he will have
to explain the Theorem of Pythagoras to boys who have never
met it before. Term after term I get this same feeling of help-
lessness. The whole thing is ridiculous. With co-operation and
proper attention even a dull form should be able to grasp the
principles involved and the main lines of the proof in an hour's
good hard work; knowledge of the construction will come with
practice. But IIIA do *not* co-operate. They are too prone to let
their minds wander, to be led astray by what are from the point
of view of geometry only side-issues, to *make*, as I am always
telling them, difficulties instead of going straight at the task and
getting it done. It is not that they are lazy. That I could deal
with, for I come down like a ton of bricks on idleness in any
shape or form. It is rather, I think, a failure to understand the
*importance* of what it is we are trying to do.

'This morning,' I said to them, 'we are going to prove that
the square on the hypotenuse of a right-angled triangle is equal
to the sum of the squares on the other two sides.'

'Is that a likely thing to happen?' Mason asked.

I told the others to be quiet and asked Mason what he
meant.

'I mean is a right-angled triangle likely to have a square on
its hypotenuse?'

'I'm afraid I don't quite follow you, Mason,' I said. 'If I
draw a right-angled triangle on the board and then draw a
square on the side opposite the right angle, it has got a square
on its hypotenuse. The question whether it is *likely* to have such
a square does not arise.'

'Not on the board, sir, no. But I mean in real life. I mean if
real-life triangles don't have squares on their hypotenuses there
wouldn't be much point in proving that they are equal to whatever it is they are equal to, would it, sir?'

'You mean "would *there*", you chump.'

'Be quiet, Etheridge,' I said.

'I see what Mason means, sir,' said Hillman. 'I mean it

would be a pretty good fluke if a triangle had squares on all its three sides at once, wouldn't it, sir?'

'There is no question of a fluke about it,' I said, beginning to lose patience. 'Now attend to me, all of you.' I then drew on the board a right-angled triangle ABC, and on the sides AB, AC and BC proceeded to construct squares ABDE, ACFG and BCHJ respectively.

'What is there funny about that, Atkins?' I asked when I had finished.

'Nothing,' he said.

'Then why laugh?'

It is a constant vexation to me that these boys seem to be amused at nothing at all. I do not want them to be glum and dispirited, of course; there are times when we all have a good laugh together and no harm is done. But this inane giggling at nothing simply holds up the work of the set. I gave Atkins a sharp warning and turned to Mason.

'Now, Mason,' I said, 'that wasn't very difficult, was it? My triangle's got squares on each of its sides.'

'My canary's got circles under its eyes,' sang a voice, and there was an immediate outburst of laughter at this piece of downright impertinence.

'Was that you, Williamson?' I demanded sternly.

'No, sir.'

'Then who was it?'

There was no reply.

'Filthy Dick passed the window just then, sir,' suggested Clarke, who sits by it. 'It must have been him.'

'He,' said Etheridge.

'You shut up, Etheridge. You don't know everything.'

'Clarke,' I cried, 'you will come and see me at the end of the period. And you too, Etheridge. I will not have these interruptions.'

'He meant the gardener's boy,' explained Mason. 'We call him Filthy Dick because he never washes. You should see his neck.'

'Never mind that now, Mason. The point is, are you prepared to admit that this figure on the board is a triangle with squares on each of its sides?'

'I suppose so, sir. Only it looks more like three squares joined together now, with a space in the middle.'

'Very well, Mason,' I said wearily. 'Let us put it that when three squares have their corners touching in such a way that the space enclosed between them is a right-angled triangle, the largest square is equal to the sum of the two smaller squares. Will that satisfy you?'

'All right by me, sir,' said Mason.

'Anything to get rid of the hypotenuse,' said Anderson.

I threw my chalk into a corner and went quietly to my desk.

'You will all,' I said, 'open your books and copy out the construction and proof of the Theorem of Pythagoras. Any boy who has not finished when the bell rings will complete the work in his spare time and show it up to me during break tomorrow morning. I am thoroughly dissatisfied with the behaviour of the whole set. Unless there is a decided improvement in the next few days you will find yourselves in pretty serious trouble. Now get on with your work in silence. Well, Atkins, what is it?'

'I think Sapoulos is crying again, sir.'

The Greek boy Sapoulos is a source of continual worry to me. The slightest thing seems to upset him. Naturally one makes allowances, as he is a stranger in a strange land and may often feel rather lonely, but it is quite ridiculous that he should break down over the most trivial matters in the way he does. I have tried being kind to him but it only seems to make matters worse, and I dare say what he really needs is a little sternness and discipline. Something to stiffen him up. On this occasion I told him not to be so silly, and asked him what the Spartans at Thermopylae would have thought of such a cry-baby.

I had forgotten, until Mason asked me what the Spartans did at Thermopylae, that none of my IIIA boys knows any Greek history. I told him how Leonidas and his gallant three hundred held a mighty Persian host at bay for days and finally died at their post rather than surrender.

'What were the Persians up to?' asked Etheridge.

I told him of Xerxes' plans to conquer Greece, and, as the boys were obviously interested, went on to describe the marshalling of the great army, the digging of the canal at Athos, the lashing of the Hellespont with chains and the building of the bridge of boats, and how Xerxes wept to think that of all his host not one man would be alive when a hundred years had passed by. I had got Xerxes as far as Therma, where the river Echeidorus was drunk dry, when to my great disappointment the bell rang. I think the boys were disappointed too, for they asked me quite eagerly to go on with the story another time.

Tomorrow we must have a real go at Pythagoras. I might begin perhaps by telling them something of the man himself and his position in the hierarchy of Greek philosophers.

## WEDNESDAY

This morning IIIA were unusually quiet when I went in and I at once glanced at the front legs of my desk. Once or twice since I first came to Burgrove I have hurt myself rather badly through my desk falling off its dais the moment I have leant my elbows on it. I shall always believe, though I have never been able to prove it, that this must have been the work of the boys. Old Poole, who left us last year after twenty-seven years' faithful service in charge of French and Geography, had the same experience, and he was positive that the front legs had been balanced deliberately on the very edge of the dais. Though, as he used to say, it might simply be carelessness on the part of the cleaner. It is always difficult to bring this kind of thing home to the boys.

. However, the desk looked all right today, but I was still uneasy. Every schoolmaster knows how unnerving it is when the boys sit quietly in their places and watch you in that silly expressionless way they have, and I do not mind admitting that I stood quite still in the middle of the floor for a full minute waiting for something to happen. Nothing happened at all except that I distinctly heard Mason whispering, '*Rigor mortis* has set in.'

I at once strode to the desk to get my punishment-book, but when I opened the lid a pigeon flew out, nearly knocking my spectacles off and giving me, naturally enough, a very nasty shock. In my seven years at Burgrove I have never had such a thing happen to me. I went white with anger.

'Stop that noise this instant!' I shouted. 'And you, Mason, leave that bird alone and go back to your desk. Now, which of you is responsible for this? Hurry up, I'm waiting.'

There was absolute silence for some seconds, until the pigeon, which had settled on top of the blackboard, began to coo in an annoying way, and I then brought my fist down with a crash on the desk.

'We had better understand one another,' I said with cold fury. 'Somebody put that pigeon in my desk and I am going to find out who did it. Unless the person responsible owns up within three minutes – Ah, Mason, so it *was* you?'

'*Me,* sir. No, sir. Only I think – '

'Well?'

'I think it's got something tied to its leg.'

Someone suggested it might be a message.

'It's a stool-pigeon!' cried Clarke.

'I bet it's spies.'

'Atkins saw a man just like Hitler behind the pavvy – '

'Be quiet!' I shouted.

While I was considering what to do, Mason, who seems utterly unable to hold his tongue for two seconds, asked whether he might find out what the message said. I asked him rather sarcastically how he proposed to catch the pigeon, and before I could object he went to the blackboard and held out his right index finger, which the bird at once settled upon. I gave Hillman fifty lines for clapping, as a warning to the others, and then suggested to Mason that he seemed to know the pigeon remarkably well. He replied that he knew all the school pigeons well and he thought this be one of them. I had already guessed this, but said nothing.

'Shall I read the message, sir?' he asked, untying it from the bird's leg.

'Very well,' I said, after a moment's hesitation. 'What does it say?'

'It says "Fly at once. All is discovered." '

In the ordinary way I might have joined in the general laughter, but this morning I felt too upset and angry.

'Give me that paper, Mason,' I said, 'and sit down. No – let that bird out of the window first. I want every boy – give out some slips, Etheridge, please, there is no need to waste a whole sheet – I want every boy to copy out what is written here and sign his name beneath it. And no talking.'

'Need *I* do it, sir?'

'Certainly you must do it, Sapoulos. And stop that silly whimpering this instant.'

The boys then began clamouring that they had forgotten the message, and to save further trouble I wrote it up on the board. My plan was of course to compare the handwriting on the slips of paper with that on the original paper; in this way I felt certain of being able to spot the culprit, though as a matter of fact, when I looked through the slips this evening I found that the boys had misunderstood my intention and written the words in capitals, which made the test practically useless. Etheridge collected the slips without incident and I then told the whole set to get on with the solving of brackets in Exercise 37. I felt too weary and disheartened to do any actual teaching.

Unless someone has owned up by tomorrow morning I shall have to take severe measures. But it is difficult to know what to do.

THURSDAY

There was an unfortunate sequel to the pigeon affair this morning. After prayers in Big School the Headmaster said he had something serious to say. It appears that when he entered Classroom 4 for the second period yesterday morning he found what he described as an impertinent message scrawled up on the board. He did not propose to repeat the message, as the boy responsible would know very well what he meant. Let that boy stand up at once and confess. I had no option but to come forward from my place with the other masters and explain that I had myself written the sentence and that I regretted the board had not been cleaned at the end of the period by the bottom boy of the set, whose duty it was. I added, for I did not wish to get Sapoulos into trouble, that the boy concerned had not yet perhaps had time to get used to our English ways and customs.

This ended the matter for the time being, but it has put me in something of a dilemma. The Headmaster, who is, if anything, a shade too inquisitive, will no doubt require a fuller explanation, and though I have managed to avoid him for the whole of today, I cannot hope to do so indefinitely. The difficulty is that I do not wish to tell him about the pigeon in my desk; it would only worry him and could do no good. He is still rather upset, to tell the truth, about my accident in the boot-room. So I shall have to think of some other reason for writing that absurd message on the board. It would be better of course if I could link it up in some way with algebra. But I don't at the moment see my way.

In the meantime I have told IIIA that I have decided to say no more about the pigeon provided nothing of the sort happens again, and I have warned them that the less they say about it to anyone the better it will be for them.

It looks as if I may have to go to the Headmaster over this row with Gilbert about his wretched potatoes. Important as his crop may be, there are other things in the world besides potatoes, as I told him. The boys did not come here, as far as I am aware, to learn potato-lifting, nor have their parents expressed a particular desire to have this subject included in the curriculum. If they had, we should very soon see it down as an Extra.

The whole thing is simply a matter of principle. If it is necessary, in the interests of discipline, to keep boys in for half an hour after lunch, then they must be kept in. The fact that Gilbert has put their names down for potato-lifting at that time is neither here nor there. He must get substitutes. Or he must lift his infernal crop at some other time. It is absolute nonsense to say that my boys get themselves kept in on purpose to miss potato-lifting. Extra school with me is no picnic, I can assure him.

Gilbert made me very angry by trying to argue that nothing was gained by keeping boys in, anyway. I told him, pretty sharply, to mind his own business. Let him use his own methods, and have the goodness to allow me to continue to use mine. Of course if he runs his 'Potato Gang', as he calls it, so badly that they will do anything to get out of it, that is another matter and is an additional argument for my speaking to the Head. His answer to this was that I could go and cry on the old Squid's shoulder all night for all he cared, and he hoped I should be rewarded by having the responsibility for the potatoes handed over to me. 'Then,' he went on (and this is what I cannot forgive), 'when your IIIA boys bombard you with ink-pots again you can give the whole lot an extra hour on the potatoes, thus killing two birds with one stone.'

I went white with anger. Even had any ink-pots been thrown, which of course was not the case, it would have been in the worst possible taste for Gilbert to refer to it. It is an unwritten law among schoolmasters not to allude in any way to any disciplinary difficulties that a colleague may be meeting in the course of his school duties. Naturally one is aware some-times, one cannot help being aware, that another master is failing to maintain strict order in his classroom. The noise in poor old Poole's room, towards the close of his time here, used to be indescribable. But one does *not* mention it, least of all to the man himself. Gilbert, in his proper senses, knows this as well as I do, just as he knows that it is nonsense to suggest that I, of all people, would allow ink-pots to be thrown about in my room. The fact is, he had lost his temper and was trying to make capital out of an accident that happened yesterday morning in my Algebra period – an accident that happened, moreover, *after* I had been obliged to tell the boys to come in for half an hour after lunch, and so had nothing to do with their punishment at all.

I kept them in, as a matter of fact, because they were rather silly and over-excited about taking out some brackets. I was showing them that the way to get rid of the brackets in an expression like $(a+b)(a-b)$ was to multiply out, resulting in $a^2-b^2$, when Mason, who is rather a thorn in my side in some ways, objected that in the previous Algebra period we had started with $a^2 - b^2$ and got it to $(a+b)\,(a-b)$.

'Yes, Mason?' I said, not quite understanding what he was driving at.

'Well, sir, now we have started with $(a+b)\,(a-b)$ and got it to $a^2 - b^2$.'

'Exactly. That shows we were right yesterday, doesn't it?'

'Yes, sir, but there doesn't seem any end to it. When it's $a^2 - b^2$ we have to work away and get it to $(a+b)\,(a-b)$ and when it is $(a+b)\,(a-b)$ you're still not satisfied, sir, and we have all the trouble of making it into $a^2 - b^2$ again, sir. Couldn't we jolly well make up our minds which is best and leave it alone, sir?'

Another boy shouted, 'It's not fair, sir,' and in a moment the whole set was talking at once, urging me to 'make up my mind' and 'leave well alone', and a lot more extravagant nonsense. One boy even had the impertinence to offer odds of three to one on $a^2 - b^2$.

When the whole form forgets itself, it is worse than useless to try to pick out particular offenders. Jump on the whole lot and teach them a good lesson. Half an hour extra does them no real harm. I used it, in this case, to explain clearly to them why it is that sometimes one wants to factorize an expression and sometimes to resolve or simplify it, taking instances from problems in real life. They rather enjoyed it, I think.

In any case, all this had nothing whatever to do with the ink-pots which Gilbert saw on the floor round my desk when he looked in to borrow my dictionary at the end of the period. I had thrown them there myself, if he only knew – for reasons I may jot down here later on, but which I certainly do not feel called upon to explain to him.

We are not on speaking terms at present, which I always think a pity on a small staff, particularly as Miss Coombes – however, there is no need to go into that now.

FRIDAY

Gilbert and Rawlinson were talking about discipline in the Common Room the other day, when we were all hanging up

our gowns after morning school, and Rawlinson suddenly said,
'You'd better ask A.J. about that. He's the expert on lines in
these parts.'

'I see nothing to laugh at in that, Rawlinson,' I said, colouring up, and I added that, although I very much disliked giving
impositions, it was sometimes necessary in order to keep the
boys up to concert pitch.

'Your IIIA lot were at concert pitch all right this morning,'
said Gilbert. 'I heard them from the Library.'

'Anyway, Rawlinson,' I said, ignoring Gilbert, who is
inclined at times to let his tongue run away with him, 'I think
it better to set a few lines than to keep a whole form in on a
fine afternoon, as some people do.'

Rawlinson, knowing very well what I meant, replied that
he had kept the Lower Fourth in because they seemed incapable of learning the second page of principal parts, not because
they had tied his boot-laces together or put soot in his waist-
coat-pockets. This silly and exaggerated reference to a forgotten incident of my apprentice-days angered me very much
and I went in to lunch without another word. My temper had
been a little frayed that morning by Matron in one of her fussy
moods. She started some long rigmarole after Prayers about
the boys' socks, and when I attempted to explain that the boys'
socks had nothing whatever to do with me she became almost
impertinent. 'Pardon me, Mr Wentworth,' she said, 'but the
boys' socks have a great deal to do with *me*' (a thing I had
never dreamed of denying), 'and I cannot possibly run my
department properly without reasonable co-operation from the
masters. What is the use of my laying out clean socks for the
boys on Sunday morning if they are to be taken out for a walk
in the afternoon through some of the muddiest places in
Wilminster? The *state* that those boys' feet were in, Mr
Wentworth! It's really too bad.' After some further inconclu-
sive talk we parted, but the incident rankled. I am here to
*teach*, not to trifle with hosiery.

I only mention this to explain why I was perhaps a little
hasty with Rawlinson later in the day.

The talk about impositions recurred to me today when

Mason showed up fifty lines I had had to give him for making an uncouth noise. As he handed them in immediately after break and I had only set them during the first period I asked him how he had managed to find time to do them, and he explained that he had done them in advance at the week-end. This aroused my suspicions and I looked more closely at the lines, only to find that they were not lines at all but some old history notes torn bodily from an exercise-book. Mason then said that he had done it as a protest against the system of giving lines, which he regarded as a rotten sort of impot. Naturally no self-respecting master can allow the boys to dictate to him the kind of punishment they prefer, and I told Mason pretty sharply to go to his desk and sit down; but what he had said, coupled with Rawlinson's remarks, made me wonder whether I could not devise some more satisfactory disciplinary measure.

After a little thought I hit on a plan. First I wrote down the names of the boys on a slip of paper. Then I held this up for them to see and explained that I proposed to mark a cross against the name of any boy who misbehaved in any way during the period. I should say nothing at the time, but if at the end of the period any boy had three crosses against his name he would be severely dealt with.

'What will happen?' asked Hillman.

'Wait and see, my friend,' I replied. I had not, as a matter of fact, made up my mind about this, but naturally I did not let the boys know. If there is one thing that really frightens them, it is suspense.

Clarke then asked whether a boy would only get one cross at a time, whatever he did.

'No, Clarke,' I replied. 'I shall give *two* crosses for impertinence'; and I immediately made two marks against his name on the list.

'That's not fair, sir,' he cried. 'I didn't know we'd begun.'

I stared at him without a word until one of us was forced to look away.

'Do you want to have a *third* cross?' I asked quietly.

He made no reply, and I turned to Atkins, who had his hand up.

'May I ask a question, sir?'

'If it is a sensible one – yes,' I said, without much hope.

'I only wondered if Sapoulos gets a cross if he cries, sir.'

'Be careful, Atkins,' I warned him, taking up my pencil, and I was glad to see that there was an immediate hush. I then proceeded with the working out of some simultaneous equations on the board, and the rest of the period passed quietly enough. Once or twice I went to my desk without a word and made an ostentatious mark on the paper, but I took care not to give any boy more than two crosses. I want more time to decide what I am going to do in cases of serious disobedience.

I was still at the board when the bell rang and several of the keener boys crowded round to ask me to explain points in the working-out that they had not understood. It was some minutes before I could get to my desk to collect my books, and when I did so I noticed at once that the punishment list had been tampered with. There were six crosses against the name of every boy except that of Sapoulos, who had twelve. No doubt the boy who did this imagined I might not notice or that I might believe I had actually made all these marks myself. He will soon learn, whoever he is, that it is a bad mistake to underrate your enemy.

I am not going to put up with this kind of thing. Tomorrow I shall tell them that they will only have themselves to thank if I go back to the old system of lines, which they appear to dislike so much. And I shall not mince my words.

SATURDAY

The whole nib question will, I think, have to be gone into rather thoroughly at our next Common Room meeting. Would it do if the boys had a box of nibs each at the beginning of term, to be kept in their desks and used as sparingly as possible on the understanding that they had to last till the end of term? C.G. says they would get through the whole lot in a fortnight. He says they use them as ballast for paper aeroplanes and so on. I know nothing about this. I don't allow paper aeroplanes, or darts for that matter, in my classroom, and what boys do in their spare time is of course no concern of mine. But I think he exaggerates. If boys are not to be trusted to look after their own nibs the school may as well close down, it seems to me. Encourage a sense of responsibility, as the Headmaster himself says, and you are half-way to the formation of real character. I believe he would be on my side in this business. The present system wastes far too much time.

This morning I was in the middle of a rather important demonstration (tangents) on the board when Hillman asked for a new nib. I told him that he did not need a nib in order to listen to a demonstration, and he replied that he would need one as soon as they started on the Riders. 'Then ask for it then,' I said. He objected that this would mean he would lose time while the others were working and would get behindhand. I saw the justice of this, but pointed out that it would have been better for everybody if he had asked for his nib at the beginning of the period instead of interrupting the lesson half-way through. He said he had only just noticed that his nib was broken; it must have got caught in the hinge of his desk while he was looking for a ruler. I might well have asked him what business he had to be looking for a ruler when he was supposed to be following my explanation on the board, but to save time I gave him a nib from the box in my desk and told him to be more careful in future.

Three more boys then came up in quick succession and asked for nibs, and as I had given one to Hillman I could not in fairness refuse them to the others. All this delay was maddening enough, but worse was to follow, for while the third boy was standing by my desk I heard a sharp cry and looked up to see Sapoulos with his head wedged in one of the lockers, while Atkins and Mason were trying to pull him out by the arms. This at any rate was the explanation given me by Mason, and I was forced to accept it, for as I stepped down from the dais I tripped somehow over my gown and fell to the floor, though not heavily, so that I was unable to see whether Sapoulos was really incapable of freeing himself or not. By the time I had recovered my feet and assured the boys who ran to my aid that I was unhurt, the incident was over and the three boys back at their desks.

Naturally I asked Sapoulos why he had gone to his locker without permission, but he was sobbing and unable to speak, so Atkins volunteered the information that Sapoulos was looking, he believed, for a pen.

I threw up my hands.

'*Where* is the boy's pen?' I demanded.

'It is in the tool-house of my gardener's aunt,' said Mason.

I never overlook impertinence, and I gave Mason a talking-to which he will, I think, remember as long as he lives. I told him that he had come to Burgrove not to be a public buffoon nor to practise the art of being rude to those who were a good deal older and perhaps even a little wiser than himself, but to learn. Presumably, I said, it was the wish of his parents who were spending their money on his education that he should fit himself for a Public School and afterwards for some useful career. At present I could see no prospect of either wish being fulfilled. He would have to pull himself together and take up a very different attitude towards his school-work if he was to have the slightest chance of getting through Common Entrance; and as for a career, unless there was an unexpected demand for third-rate comedians, I could not see any way in which the world would be likely to make use of his services. 'There will have to be a big change, Mason,' I told him, 'or you and I will find ourselves at loggerheads.'

'*You* may,' he said. '*I'm* going to Cheltenham.'

I sent him out of the room at once, and when he had gone Clarke asked for some blotting-paper, which I refused. We masters always have enough nibs in our desk for the boys' needs, but pens and blotting-paper are kept in the stationery cupboard of which Rawlinson holds the key. This means that in order to gain access to the pens and so on, except at the stated times on Mondays, Wednesdays and Fridays when the cupboard is open, one has to send a chit for whatever one wants to Rawlinson. This I was not prepared to do merely to provide Clarke with blotting-paper, especially as every boy has a clean sheet put on his desk every Monday morning. Rawlinson is not particularly keen on receiving chits during morning school, and the row I had with him over the pegs in the changing-room makes me chary of asking favours. So I tore my own blotting-paper in half and gave a piece to Clarke. He made it into a dart, which I confiscated according to my invariable rule.

We then turned our attention to the angular relationship between tangents and radii.

Mason came in while I was busy with the large wooden compasses we use for work on the board and said he was sorry if he had been rude. He said he was playing for the Second Eleven that afternoon and was rather excited. I told him I was glad to hear he had been chosen, but that he must try to remember that football was not the important thing in life. Work must come first.

This, for some reason, made all the boys laugh.

A boy called Phillips got into my bad books this afternoon. It was too wet for football after all (which was hard luck on Mason) so we all put on our macs and went for a walk, Gilbert taking the Seniors round by Fotherham Dyke, while the Juniors came with me for a ramble in Marling Woods. Sapoulos and young Hopgood asked if they might walk with me and I consented, since I like to give this privilege to all the boys in turn, and Hillman, who also asked, had the position on my right as recently as three weeks ago. I always make a note of these things; boys are so quick to notice any unfairness or favouritism.

Well, I was talking to Hopgood about footer when a boy came running back to say that Phillips was stuck in a drain and couldn't move. (I say running *back* because of course we masters always keep behind when taking a walk; it is the best place to keep an eye on the boys, see that they are wearing their caps properly and so on. The young rascals take them off and put them in their pockets if they get half a chance, which is against the School rules.)

'Phillips has no business to be in a drain at all, as you know perfectly well, Clarke,' I said brusquely; but none the less I hurried off after him as fast as I could.

We found the whole walk collected at a point where a

shallow but muddy stream runs under the path through a circular drain or culvert some twelve to fifteen feet in length. I at once ordered the boys to stand away from all that mud and, pushing them aside, lowered myself cautiously to the level of the water. Then, clinging with my left hand to a convenient stump of wood, I bent down and peered into the drain. I could see nothing at all owing to the darkness, so I said, 'Come out of there at once, Phillips, d'you hear?' It had struck me immediately that he might very well be playing the fool and merely pretending to be stuck. However, there was no reply, and I repeated the order in a louder tone.

'Perhaps he'd hear better if you went round to the other end, sir,' suggested Mason, who was watching from the other side of the stream. 'His head's facing that way.'

'Just *look* at your boots, Mason!' I cried. 'Whatever will Matron say?'

I did not catch his reply, for at this moment the stump unluckily gave way and I was precipitated into the water. Instinctively I thrust out both hands as I fell, but, remembering my wrist-watch just in time, drew back my right arm without realizing that this would inevitably throw me forwards on my head. As it turned out I rolled completely over and thus failed after all to save the watch from a ducking. But by a miracle I kept my wallet dry.

'What did you say, Mason?' I asked as I rose.

'Nothing, sir.'

This I knew to be an untruth, but in the circumstances it seemed best to pass it over. Accordingly I showed my displeasure only by a look and, scrambling up the bank, made my way through a crowd of gaping boys to the other end of the culvert. Here there was no difficulty, for the bank was less steep and, my boots being already full of water, I was able to stand boldly in midstream. Almost at once I made out the white glimmer of Phillips' face just beyond a kind of iron grating which must no doubt have arrested his progress.

'Is that you, Phillips?' I asked.

'Yes, sir.'

'May I ask what you think you are doing in there?'

'I'm stuck, sir.'

'Possibly,' I said. 'Where are you stuck?'

'At the back, sir. My coat got rucked up when I tried to go back, sir, and I think – I'm not sure, sir, but I think my braces are caught on the roof, sir.'

'Are your feet wet?'

'A bit, sir.'

'Tut!' I said. 'This is a bad business, Phillips. How long have you been here?'

'About five minutes, sir.'

'Don't be ridiculous, boy!' I said angrily. 'I mean how long have you been at the School?'

'Oh, four terms, sir.'

'Quite long enough to know better,' I said sternly, and told him to stay where he was until he was released.

I then called the boys to me and told them that Phillips was caught by his braces at the back, and as his feet were wet he must be got out at once or there might be serious consequences. I explained that I was too large to enter the drain, and that one of them must therefore volunteer to crawl in at the end where – at the end which I had first investigated, and attempt to free Phillips' braces.

'Can I do it, sir?'

'Very well, Mason,' I said, 'but take off your shoes and stockings and roll up your trousers. I cannot have the whole Junior School soaking wet.'

It was an anxious time for us all while Mason was in the drain, but eventually he reappeared and clambered up the bank.

'Well, Mason?' I cried eagerly.

'I've freed his braces, sir,' he cried, holding them up.

'Mason,' I said in my coldest voice. 'This is no time for joking. Where is Phillips?'

'In the drain, sir. He daren't come out.'

Mason explained that Phillips had decided to stay in the drain because he was afraid of being punished when he came out. He said – Mason said, that is – that he thought if Phillips

knew for certain nothing would happen to him he would come
out at once.

'Did you suggest this to him, Mason?' I asked sternly.

'Me, sir? Good lord, no sir!'

'Tell him to come out this instant,' I cried, losing all patience
with the lot of them, 'or I'll report him to the Headmaster for
a thrashing.'

When Phillips came out and I saw the state of his clothes
and the muddy boots of the other boys into the bargain I was
in despair.

'I'd like to know what Matron will have to say about this,'
I said, half to myself.

Mason, who can never learn to mind his own business,
chipped in at once. 'Wouldn't it be easiest, sir,' he suggested,
'to explain that you fell into the stream and we all got a bit
dirty helping you out?'

'Very easy indeed, Mason,' I replied sarcastically, 'if you
can think of any reason why I *should* have fallen into the
stream.'

'Need there be a special reason, sir?'

'Am I the kind of person who goes about falling into streams
for no reason whatever?' I asked.

'We – ell . . .' said Mason.

I gave him a thundering good wigging for that piece of
impertinence.

SUNDAY

'Please, sir, how do you spell "codger"?'

Among the tasks of the master on duty on Sundays is invigilation during the boys' letter-writing hour after morning
chapel; though invigilation is not the right word perhaps, since
one does not have to look out for cribbing or anything of that
sort. One is there to help and to see that the boys keep quiet
and get on with their letters. Naturally, if there was any cribbing, I mean if one boy was leaning over to see what the next
boy was writing, one would put a stop to it, because they ought
to be able to think of something to say to their parents on their
own. Besides, we believe in the boys' correspondence being

absolutely private – letters are not read and censored here or any of that nonsense, I am glad to say.

The boy who asked me to help with his spelling was young Fraser (red hair and freckles) and for a moment I failed to follow him. ' "Codger", Fraser?' I repeated. 'What sort of codger?'

'Silly old codger,' said Mason.

There was nothing to get hold of about that, really, though I half suspected impertinence. 'Well, Fraser?' I remarked, brushing Mason's interruption aside. 'Do you particularly want to use that word? Not that there's anything against it,' I added with a smile, 'except that it's slang, of course, and rather old-fashioned slang at that.'

Some silly boy asked whether 'Geezer' would be more up to date, but I signalled to him to be quiet, and to save further argument spelled out Fraser's word. I had just returned to my book, a most interesting biography of Gustavus Adolphus, about whom I have often wondered, when another boy asked me how to spell 'coot'.

I looked up to find the whole school watching me.

'Get on, get on, you others,' I warned them. 'Are you writing nature notes, Parkinson?'

He said he was not, going rather red in the face for some reason.

'But, all the same, you wish to tell your parents something about coots, is that it?'

'Only about one, sir.'

'I see,' I said. 'A particular coot. What is there funny in that, Mason?'

'Nothing, sir.'

'Then why laugh?'

'I don't know, sir. Sir, are they really mad as well as bald, sir?'

'Stop this silly laughter immediately,' I cried, and almost at once the hubbub died down. To my surprise Mason persisted with his question, which I had not been intending to take seriously.

'Sir, why *do* people say he's as mad as a coot, sir?' he asked.
'It's an awfully funny sort of thing to say, isn't it, sir?'

'Sir, there's a book about a pig,' began Tremayne excitedly
(he is not one of my IIIA boys, of course), but I cut him short.
'That will do, all of you,' I said sharply. 'Sensible questions are
one thing, but we cannot spend the whole hour discussing the
habits of coots. Or pigs either,' I added, with a glance at
Tremayne. 'It's twenty past already.'

When Pettigrew asked me how many bats there were in
'belfry' I decided the thing was getting beyond a joke. 'No
more questions for ten minutes,' I ordered. 'Any boy who is in
difficulties can come up to my desk at the end of that time and
ask me quietly.'

Quite a number of boys came up when the ten minutes were
over, and I was explaining to de Groot about postal rates to
Holland (a schoolmaster has to be an expert on a hundred and
one things nowadays. Goodness knows what poor old Poole
would have made of it all – he was French master here for a
number of years until the boys put salt in his hair. There were
one or two other contretemps as a matter of fact; the Headmaster might have overlooked an isolated incident). Well, I
was talking to de Groot, as I was saying, when an infernal
shindy broke out about half-way down the queue.

'Stop that scrimmaging about there,' I shouted. 'Fraser,
what are you doing?'

'Somebody hacked me on the heel, sir.'

'Sneak,' said Mason.

'It isn't sneaking to say "somebody".'

'Oh, no! Considering nobody could have hacked you
except the next man in the queue.'

'You're sneaking yourself now,' said Fraser.

I put my spectacles down firmly on the desk and rose to my
feet.

'Go to your desks all of you,' I said quietly. 'I will not have
this ridiculous arguing and bickering during Letter-Hour. You
can all just get on with it straight away without any more fuss.
And *stop* fiddling with that watch, Jenkins. You've written
practically nothing.'

Jenkins is a new boy, who probably hasn't had a watch of his own before, but all the same he has been here long enough now to know that he must not fiddle with it in class, or in Letter-Hour, which comes to the same thing. He told me, feebly, that he didn't know what to say.

'My dear boy,' I replied. 'Surely you can write your own letters home. This is not supposed to be Dictation period. Tell them what you did last week. Tell them what is going to happen next week, if you like.'

'*Is* anything going to happen next week?' asked Mason.

I always try to avoid sarcasm, but this was too much. 'Considering the School plays Fox House away on Wednesday and on Thursday there is a lecture on the Ice Age – '

'With slides?' asked some fool.

' – and the second monthly form-order will be out at the week-end, even you, Mason,' I continued smoothly, 'can hardly regard next week as a complete blank. What boy interrupted me just now?'

Nobody owned up, so I put on a Silence rule. 'Anybody who speaks in this room without my permission,' I told them, 'will get a hundred lines.' You could have heard a pin drop. I did hear a nib, as a matter of fact – Mason of course. But I had my eye on him, and he bent down and picked it up without a word. Then, as ill-luck would have it, Miss Coombes came in with some music lists.

'Oh, Mr Wentworth,' she began, but the rest of the sentence was lost in a gale of laughter in which, I am ashamed to say, I could not refrain from joining. Somehow the idea of coming down on poor Miss Coombes with a hefty impot was irresistibly comic.

She went very red in the face and marched out without another word, not understanding the joke, of course. I am afraid she will be upset, though I shall make a point of explaining things to her after lunch, naturally.

The absurd incident had one good effect, for the boys settled down straight away, everybody scribbling away quite contentedly for the rest of the hour. I had my suspicions of what they were all writing about – suspicions which were pretty well confirmed when, right at the end, Fraser asked me how to spell embarrassed.

'Two "r's", Fraser,' I told him, and was unable to resist adding, 'The "ass", no doubt you are familiar with?'

The boys were quick to appreciate my little dig at him and everybody laughed. They laughed still more when Fraser replied, 'Yes, thank you, sir. I've got him down already,' though I confess I failed to see the point.

Anyway, I hope they won't say anything derogatory about Miss Coombes in their letters. She is a friendly soul, though inclined to be a little weak – of which the boys, I have reason to think, sometimes take advantage.

# Lent Term 1939
# The Man Faggott

After the bustle and excitement of the first day of term it was a real shock to me to be informed quite casually by Gilbert this morning that he is taking over eleven o'clock milkers. Eleven o'clock milkers is our name here for the distribution of milk during break to certain boys whose parents have expressed a wish that they should have it, and for years it has been my prerogative to tick off the names of these boys as they come up for their glasses. The last thought in my mind as I entered Common Room after breakfast was that any change could be contemplated in this arrangement – certainly not without consulting me.

Of course I went straight off to the Headmaster the moment I heard of it.

I found him interviewing some parents who had brought their boy, a new boy, down a day late, and would have withdrawn at once, but Mr Saunders beckoned me in.

'Ah, Wentworth!' he cried, 'I'm glad you looked in. Mr Wentworth is one of our little community of assistant masters, Mrs Carter – a very happy little community, eh, Wentworth? I'm sure he will help Johnny all he can.'

'How do you do, Mrs Carter?' I said. 'We will certainly do our best to put young Johnny on the right road. You need have no doubt that he will be happy here at Burgrove – and work hard, won't you, Johnny?'

The little boy made no reply, and I turned to his father.

'Why, Mr Carter,' I exclaimed admiringly, 'he's the living image of you!'

'I should have introduced you,' put in Mrs Carter, colouring prettily. 'This is Captain Ferguson, a very kind friend who motored us down.'

It would have been the work of a moment to cover up this little misunderstanding, but in stepping backwards to address a remark about the mild weather to Mrs Carter I had the misfortune to tread on her boy's foot; he had somehow got round behind me in that irritating way young people have. Naturally I apologized, but he burst into tears, and indeed made a most unnecessary fuss about the incident.

'Come, come, Johnny,' I said kindly. 'You are a big boy now. You must learn to put up with a few hard knocks now you have come to Burgrove.'

'Why is that, Mr Wentworth?' cried his mother, mistaking my meaning. 'Do you make a point of treading on the boys' feet at this school?'

'No, Mrs Carter,' I replied, turning the point neatly though perfectly politely, against her. 'We teach the boys to stand on their *own* feet at Burgrove.'

'Well, Wentworth,' said the Headmaster, rather shortly for him, 'is there anything you want to see me about?'

'Nothing that will not keep until you are free, thank you, Headmaster,' I replied, and with a smile that included them all I turned on my heel and walked into a maidenhair fern which Mr Saunders, rashly as I think, keeps on a tall stand by the door. Only great quickness on my part saved the pot from falling to the floor, and finding myself with the fern in my arms I decided that the best thing to do was to walk straight out with it, pretending that I had meant all along to take it with me. This naturally made it impossible for me to shut the door, and thus as I walked through the swing-door into the boys' part of the house I overheard Mrs Carter make a remark which I greatly resented. Nothing is to be gained by repeating it here.

I had a busy day and had almost forgotten the trifling annoyances of the morning, when the Headmaster summoned me to his study.

'Well, Wentworth,' he began, 'have you any explanation to offer?'

'Explanation?' I stammered.

'Of your rudeness to one of our parents and your extra-ordinary action in removing an ornament from my room with-out permission and without explanation of any kind?'

'If you are referring to the maidenhair fern,' I replied, con-trolling myself with difficulty, 'I can only say that I should have thought my reasons for taking it were obvious.'

'Not to me,' he said, and added that even if he could con-ceive some object for which a fern was necessary in my day's work, as for example to illustrate some scientific point to the boys or as a drawing model – though it would be news to him to learn that I was concerned with the teaching either of science or drawing at Burgrove, even so he still could not imagine that the need was of such urgency as to justify the methods I had adopted to acquire one. He had heard, he went on, of men subject to sudden ungovernable impulses which made the possession of some desired object a paramount con-sideration, but if that was the explanation he only wished I had given him some inkling of my desire for a maidenhair fern. He could then have had one placed in my room at the beginning of term and this deplorable incident would have been avoided. But on the whole, he said, he preferred to think that my action was simply a particularly mistaken and ill-timed piece of clowning.

'If that is what you think, Headmaster,' I burst out at last, 'I have no option but to resign my position here. I have spent many happy, and I like to think not unproductive, years at Burgrove, and I shall be sorry, more than sorry, to go – '

'We shall be sorry to lose you, Wentworth.'

'There is no reason why you *should* lose me,' I rejoined warmly. 'The whole ridiculous incident has been magnified out of all proportion. I will go and fetch this precious fern *now*. That I should be accused at my age of kleptomania and – and clownishness – is incredible!'

Blind with rage I turned to the door, but as ill luck would have it, caught my foot against the fern-stand and went down heavily against a table of silver spoons and other small bric-àbrac. When I rose to my feet, still automatically clutching the stand, there were tears of mortification in my eyes.

'Headmaster – ' I began.

'Leave me the stand, Wentworth,' he cried, 'at least leave me the stand!' and to my amazement I saw that he was smiling.

I would have spoken, but he checked me with a gesture.

'Never mind about it now,' he said. 'We'll talk about it later. And let me have my fern back when you've finished with it, won't you?'

I said good night, and as I walked away an explosion of laughter followed me down the corridor. I went to my room to write up this diary with my mind in a whirl.

### WEDNESDAY, 1 FEBRUARY

[*The following account of an incident, not mentioned in Mr Wentworth's diary, has been sent to me by Mr Charles Gilbert, one of his colleagues. It sheds a certain light on some of the pitfalls of the profession.*]

I hear that old ass Wentworth has been sending you extracts from his precious diary, though what he hopes to gain by it goodness only knows. But I don't suppose for a moment he has made any mention of the great Night Alarm – one of his finest exploits, and I thought you might like to know about it.

Well, one night I was sitting in my room down at the Masters' Cottage taking my boots off and fearing no evil, when I heard a great disturbance next door, and in a moment Wentworth came tearing in with an incoherent story about not being able to get into bed and how he'd make trouble for Mrs Barnett over this in the morning. I went along with him to investigate and, as I'd rather expected, found he'd got an apple-pie bed. As I say, I wasn't surprised because as a matter of fact I'd made it myself, but what did astonish me was that Wentworth obviously didn't know what it was. That's the trouble with him. You never can gauge the depths of the man's simplicity. He seemed to think that Mrs Barnett, who does for us at the cottage, had made a hash of her job when she made up the bed, and he was absolutely set on putting her through it for

what he called her 'abominable carelessness'. Naturally I
didn't want Mrs Barnett to be unjustly accused, so I explained
that sometimes people went into other people's rooms and
turned up the bottom sheet in this way simply in order to
surprise the owner of the room when he went to bed. 'Just as a
joke,' I added.

'But who could have done such a senseless thing?' he asked.

He looked quite upset about it, so I shook my head. But I
thought there was no harm in mentioning that I'd seen
Collingridge hanging about the cottage just after dinner.

'Collingridge!' said Wentworth. 'I thought he had more
sense.' You could see the idea came as quite a shock to him, but
after a while I persuaded him that the only way to settle it was
to go straight up to Collingridge's room and tax him with it.
'Pull the bedclothes off him, A.J.,' I said. 'Then he'll leave you
alone in future.'

In the end he put some clothes on and set off. Collingridge
sleeps up at the school, because there's no room in the cottage,
and my idea was that he'd just about have had time to clear
out the holly I'd put in his bed and get settled down for the
night before Wentworth arrived. Then if Wentworth took my
advice and whipped the clothes off him I thought there might
possibly be some fun. . . .

The last thing I expected to hear was the fire-alarm going.

What happened apparently was this. Wentworth, with his
peculiar genius for taking the wrong turning and a good deal
aided by the fact that all the lights in the school corridors are
switched off at half-past ten, went slap into Matron's room,
which lies relatively in the same position on the right at the top
of the main stairs as Collingridge's room does on the left. He
got out again, he says, before she got to the light-switch, but her
screams must have upset him because he ran too much to the
right and came a most frightful purler over a row of enamel
water-jugs they put out along the wall of the corridor ready for
the morning. Well, you know the kind of noise a lot of empty
enamelware makes when you start it rolling about the floor and
down the stairs. Wentworth, I should imagine lost his nerve

altogether, and it must have been more luck than judgement that made him bolt into Collingridge's room.

Collingridge, who had had about enough of all this disturbance, hit him a tremendous wallop with a pillow just as Matron set the fire alarm going.

I'm told there was a fair amount of pandemonium. The rule is that on hearing the alarm at night all boys are to put on their dressing-gowns and proceed in an orderly manner to the gymnasium – unless, I suppose, the gymnasium happens to be on fire; but I don't believe there's any provision for that. All I know is that when I got to the gym everybody seemed to be talking at once, and in the middle of it Matron was trying to explain to the Headmaster, who looks a good deal less impressive in a check dressing-gown, that there wasn't any fire but that somebody, or so she thought – though she might have been mistaken – had attempted to get into her bedroom. ('Get back to your dormitories, all you boys,' said the Reverend Saunders at this point.) Anyway, what *had* alarmed her and made her feel it was her duty, to the boys if not to herself, to ring the alarm, was a terrible noise as if some kind of wild beast were crashing and rolling about among the hot-water jugs in the corridor.

The moment old Saunders heard this about the jugs he began to look round for Wentworth. The fact is that whenever you hear a loud crash at Burgrove or see a pile of play-boxes or bowler-hats toppling to the ground you instinctively expect to catch sight of Wentworth making an unobtrusive disappearance round a corner, and you are very rarely disappointed. Wentworth wasn't in the gym, as he should have been after a fire-alarm, and I thought it only right to point out that Collingridge wasn't there either. 'No doubt,' I said, 'there is some perfectly good reason for their absence.'

There was. It became painfully clear, to me at least, what was detaining them as soon as we reached the top of the main stairs, but to the others I dare say the thudding sounds that came from the direction of Collingridge's room only made the mystery more mysterious.

'Odd!' said the Headmaster, pausing. 'Very odd. Do you think I should go in?'

For myself, I thought it far better that he shouldn't, but on the spur of the moment I could think of no argument to support this view. So I nodded dumbly and followed him in.

What old Saunders expected to see I have no idea, but I am pretty certain that it never struck him he might be intruding on a death-grapple between two of his assistant-masters. The room was a shambles, but it was the combatants who took the eye. At the moment of our entry they had got themselves into a corner beyond the bed, where Collingridge, with his head in Wentworth's stomach, was trying with a conscientiousness one could not help admiring to thrust him into a cupboard obviously two or three sizes too small for him. Wentworth, a good deal handicapped by having a sheet over his head and both feet practically off the ground, was contenting himself with belabouring his opponent's back with his fists, but I must say he was making a sound job of it.

'*Get* in there, can't you?' Collingridge was saying, butting hard.

'Ouch!' said Wentworth.

'*Wentworth!*' cried the Headmaster in an awful voice. 'Are you mad?'

The question that so many have asked themselves at various stages of Wentworth's career might have been answered then and there if only the old boy hadn't been too short of wind and too much bothered by the sheet to reply. While they were getting themselves disentangled and Wentworth was doing his bashful utmost to scrape the cupboard off his back, I took my leave. I thought that they could probably explain the whole thing between them without any help from me.

But, as I told Wentworth next morning, he'll really have to learn to control his passions a bit better or he'll be getting the sack. Of course I was referring to his scrap with Collingridge, but for some reason of his own he chose to think I meant the Matron. You never saw a man in such a lather.

[*This concludes Mr Gilbert's narrative.*]

TUESDAY, 14 FEBRUARY

People ask me sometimes whether I find the schoolboy of today noticeably quieter and more mature than his elder brother of, say, the early thirties. I cannot see it. I detect precious little difference in the young rascals. More knowledgeable perhaps on some subjects, aircraft modelling to take an obvious instance, but as bone-headed as ever over the important things. I can still twist their tails with a simultaneous quadratic; and it is still just as difficult to make them see that unless they stick to a problem, really worry at it, for themselves, instead of throwing up their hands and shouting 'Sir, Sir,' at the slightest set-back, they will never make mathematicians.

And the *time* we waste. Yesterday, after break, I told Set IIIA to write down one third as a decimal.

'Everybody finished?' I asked.

'No, sir,' said Mason.

I gave him another half-minute and then told him to stop.

'But it *won't* stop, sir.'

Everybody laughed.

'I mean it goes on and on, sir, and if I stop before it does my answer won't be right.'

'What have you got, Mason?'

'Well, sir, so far I've got point three three three three three three three three three three three three three three three three – that's correct to sixteen decimal places, sir.'

'There's nothing to laugh about!' I said sharply. 'What have you got there, Atkins?'

'Me, sir? Point three recurring, sir.'

'I am not asking for the answer to the sum. I am asking you what you have got in your right hand.'

'Nothing, sir.'

Boys invariably try this answer first, though they must know they have precious little chance of getting away with it with an old hand like me. Atkins had that boiled look that tells you at once when a boy is caught out.

'Bring it up here, Atkins,' I said. 'And the rest of you express point seven three five as a fraction.'

I wrote it up on the board to stop endless questions and then took the piece of paper Atkins handed to me.

He had simply scribbled the headmaster's name, 'Rev. Gregory Saunders, M.A.', on the paper, and I was about to send him back to his desk with a caution against wasting the time of the form when I noticed that the paper was folded over at the bottom.

'An old dodge, Atkins,' I said, unfolding it.

He had written 'The Beast of Burgrove' under the head-master's name, a serious offence.

'I can't possibly overlook this, Atkins,' I told him sternly.

'Couldn't you overlook it on his birthday, sir?' asked Mason.

'Is it your birthday, Atkins?' I asked.

'No, sir.'

'In that case, Mason, I fail to see the point of your remark. Even if it was any business of yours – '

'I was only wondering, sir, whether if it *had* been his birth-day, it would have made any difference.'

'Mason!' I warned him. 'That will do. When I want your advice about the way to treat people on their birthday, I will ask for it. Birthdays make no difference to the fact that we've all come here to work, and the sooner everyone realizes that the better.'

'Is it your birthday, sir?' somebody called out, and there was an immediate chorus of cries from the other boys. 'Jolly good, Duce,' 'Wake up, Duce,' 'Have some macaroni, Benito,' and a lot more nonsense of the same kind, which I very soon stamped on. Benito is not the boy's real name, of course (though we have quite a number of French and Belgians here now, besides Sapoulos, the Greek; and a little Dutch boy called de Groot came last term); but the others call him that because of some fancied resemblance to the Italian leader.

'Now then,' I said. 'Let's see who's got this fraction right. Otterway?'

'Not quite ready yet, sir.'

'Hurry up, boy. Trench?'

'Well, sir, I've done it, only it seems rather an absurd answer.'

'Never mind that,' I said. 'I'm used to absurd answers. What is it?'

'A hundred and forty-seven over two hundred.'

'What's absurd about that? Well, Williamson?'

'I thought I heard the bell, sir.'

I slammed my book down on the desk.

'If you would kindly attend to your work, instead of listening for the school bell, we might conceivably get through a fraction of what we have to do before the end of term – perhaps even a hundred and forty-seven two hundredths of it, Trench.'

'Jolly good, sir!' said Mason.

I told them they might go, and began to collect my things for my English period.

'May I go too, sir?' asked Atkins, about whom, I am bound to confess, I had rather forgotten.

I took up a piece of chalk and tossed it in the air.

'What are we going to do about this, Atkins?' I said. 'Eh?'

'I don't know, sir. I'm sorry, sir.'

'H'm!' I said, not knowing either. 'I'll have to think about it.'

I shall probably decide to do nothing in the end. The boy has had a good fright, which is the main thing.

WEDNESDAY, I MARCH

Rawlinson is down with flu and a man called Faggott has come in for a week or two. He is a Major apparently – one of those stocky red-faced men with a moustache which sprouts out in a disagreeable way over uneven yellow teeth. He whistles too, and is – well, more abrupt in manner towards some of the regular staff than one altogether expects or relishes. No doubt it is difficult to get the right type of man for such a short appointment, but still – there are agencies and so on which cater for this kind of emergency. One wonders if he has had much experience really; and I'm bound to say the one place one does hear of his having been at doesn't seem to me to be quite – though it's easy enough to get a false impression of these things. 'Not the way we used to do things at Marston House' – if he's said that once in the last three days he's said

it a hundred times. As if we cared how they choose to do things
at some potty little seaside school or other. 'All I can say is,' I
remarked at last, goaded beyond endurance by some petty
criticism of one of our school rules – he had chosen to be
offensive, if I remember rightly, because the boys here line up
in their school order when the bell rings for meals and march
to their places in an orderly fashion (a thoroughly wise
arrangement, as it happens) – 'All I can say is,' I remarked, 'if
that's not the way you used to do it at Marston House, so much
the worse for Marston House'; and I walked straight in to my
place at Gainsborough (each table in the dining-room is known
by the name of a famous artist or soldier – another old custom
that Faggott has not hesitated to make the subject of his stupid
pleasantries) without giving him a chance to reply. I was
thoroughly angry.

Then this morning I told him in a perfectly friendly way
that the Headmaster did not expect to see masters smoking in
the school corridors or classrooms, though of course it was quite
all right in Common Room. 'Rats to that!' he said, and strolled
off down the passage with his foul, stumpy little pipe clamped
firmly between his teeth. What can one do with such a fellow?

It is worse down at the Cottage. This evening he came
barging into my room with a bottle of whisky in his hand
looking for soda. 'This chap Rawlinson doesn't seem to have
any in his room,' he said. Rawlinson is in the San, so Faggott
has been given his room. It was on the tip of my tongue to say
that Rawlinson had probably locked up his soda, and would,
no doubt, if he had known who was to take his place, have
locked up his whisky as well; but instead I merely replied that
I had no soda to offer him and went quietly on with my
correction of IIIA's work. I had a great deal to do and my
manner ought to have made it clear to anyone that I was busy
and wished to be left alone. But a nod is as good as a wink to
a blind horse. Major Faggott wandered about the room,
whistling between his teeth, examining my belongings in the
coolest possible fashion, picking up a book here and a book
there and laying it down again with a groan, pausing with
sharp exclamations of disgust in front of my Van Gogh repro-

ductions and my college groups, going so far even as to take
up a photograph of my sister from the mantelpiece and replace
it without comment behind the ormolu clock.

'Well,' I said at last when I could stand it no longer, 'you
don't appear to have much work to do.'

He came and leaned over my shoulder. ' 'Ullo, 'ullo!' he
said, draggling his pipe-stem over the papers. 'Those curly
brackets ought to have been taken out, or I'm a Dutchman.
Three out of five.'

'Are you a mathematician, Major Faggott?'

'Me!' he said. 'You've heard of the Binomial Theorem?'

'I should hope so,' I said stiffly.

'Well, I invented it.'

'Indeed!' I said, making no attempt to keep the contempt
out of my voice. 'I was under the impression that it was
invented by Omar Khayyám.'

He roared with laughter. 'What a queer old buffer it is!
Haven't you ever read the *Rubaiyat*?'

'I have,' I answered. 'I have also read *Alice in Wonderland*.
It is quite possible for a man to be a writer as well as a mathematician – just as it should be possible for a man to be a gentleman as well as a schoolmaster.'

'It isn't,' he said, quite failing to see the implication of my
remark; 'that's why I've practically given up schoolmastering.'

I made no reply, contenting myself with ostentatiously
marking my papers, and there was silence for a long time, so
that I began to hope the man had gone. But when at last I
turned round in my chair I saw him still fiddling with the
things on my mantelpiece.

'No photograph of the Matron, I see,' he said with an
unpleasant grin.

I rose to my feet and demanded to know what he meant by
that remark. He then made a suggestion so offensive that for a
moment I was unable to speak, while the hot blood mounted
to my cheeks. Never in all my years at Burgrove have I been
spoken to in such a way – and by such a preposterous bounder.
It is typical of the man that he misinterpreted my natural flush
of indignation and was pleased to describe it as a 'guilty blush'.

I believe I might have struck him where he stood, but fortunately he saw that I was in a dangerous mood and decided to take his leave.

'Well,' he said with an attempt at nonchalance, 'if you've no soda in this rat-trap I may as well be pushing along,' and he swaggered off, turning a photograph of my old College Eight to the wall as he went out.

I went straight along to Gilbert's room as soon as he had gone. The fact is that that reference of Faggott's to a silly incident of a few weeks ago was the last straw. The whole thing was too childish. I simply tripped up in the dark one night when I was on my way to ask Collingridge about something or other, and Matron, whose room is not far away, was frightened by the noise and rang the fire-alarm. Some silly fool has exaggerated the story and told it to this impossible Faggott, who is not above twisting the whole thing round to suit his own purposes and make me look ridiculous, or worse. So I have put the whole position before Gilbert and he agrees that something must be done to put the Major – if he is a Major, which I begin to doubt – in his place. We have a sort of a plan which we think may make it clear to the Headmaster that Faggott is not at all the type for a school of this sort. Better have nobody at all until Rawlinson comes back, as I said to Gilbert, than allow a mischief-maker like Faggott the run of the place for another fortnight. I could take Rawlinson's lot with my own, if it comes to that. The desks from both classrooms would have to be moved into the gym, I suppose, though that might interfere with the Sergeant's fencing-classes. Still, fencing isn't everything.

Gilbert approved of my gym plan when I told him of it and suggested I might invigilate from the vaulting-horse – but I don't think he was serious.

MONDAY, 6 MARCH

The man Faggott continues to be a thorn in my side. Naturally as the next senior master I expected to be put in charge of the stationery cupboard during Rawlinson's absence; but Faggott, so he says, was definitely instructed by the Headmaster when he took up his temporary position here to perform all Rawlinson's duties as far as possible, and it is typical of the man's dog-in-the-manger attitude that he insists on interpreting the phrase to cover the supervision of stationery, despite his obvious lack of experience at work of this kind. This morning being Monday the cupboard was open from 9.0 to 9.30, and I thought it best to keep an eye on Faggott while the boys were coming up in turn for their requirements. As I expected, it was not long before I saw him handing out some of the special pink blotting-paper which is kept for Common Room use.

I thought it my duty to step forward and put him right at once, though I was careful to speak in a low voice in order not to discredit him in front of the boys.

'White blotting-paper?' he said, affecting to misunderstand me, and he handed me a couple of sheets without troubling to turn round.

'I do not require blotting-paper, thank you,' I said curtly.

'You soak it up yourself, eh?' he replied, accompanying this meaningless remark with a wink which made my temper rise at once. But in view of the presence of a number of boys I controlled myself and merely said it was good news to hear Rawlinson would be up again in a day or two. I think he knew what I meant.

After this it was particularly galling to hear his praises sung so loudly by IIIA during the first period after break. Apparently he has been currying favour with the boys by means of a certain facility he has for mechanical repairs, and also (and less surprisingly to those who know him) by boasting of his exploits in the Great War. Boys are extraordinarily easily taken in by men of his – I had almost said 'flashy' – type. As a result I was obliged to listen to a long account from Atkins of how Faggott had tunnelled his way out of a German fortress with a pen-knife, or some such nonsense, and when that was over Mason showed me a watch he had mended, and Hillman brought up a mechanical crane which had been newly soldered – not too well, in my opinion, though I am no artisan – just above the base. I told Hillman, rather abruptly, for I was getting tired of all this, that the classroom was no place for cranes, and a voice immediately said, 'Or pigeons' – an impertinent reference, or so I took it, to an occasion last term when a pigeon mysteriously flew out of my desk.

'Stand up the boy who said that !' I cried, and to my surprise the whole class rose to their feet. However, I am too old a hand not to recognize a concerted attempt at ragging when I see it, and I promptly decided to play them at their own game and beat them at it.

'You all said it?' I asked, only slightly raising my eyebrows. 'Very well, then, you will all be punished. A hundred lines each by tomorrow morning.'

There was a chorus of 'Oh, sirs !' which I immediately suppressed by a threat to double the imposition, and Mason then asked whether Sapoulos had to do the lines as well. I had failed to notice that the little Greek boy had remained sitting while the others got up, and my suspicions were immediately aroused.

'Did you say it, Sapoulos?' I asked sternly.

'I beg to be excused, sir,' he replied.

There was a general laugh at his quaint English, but knowing that he meant to say, 'I beg your pardon?' I repeated my question: 'Did you say "Or pigeons"?'

' "Orpigeons", sir?'

'You heard what I said.'

Sapoulos, instead of replying, kept repeating 'orpigeons, orpigeons, orpigeons' over to himself in a puzzled tone until I lost all patience with the boy.

'Sapoulos !' I thundered, 'did you or did you not say "Or pigeons"?'

The silly boy, as I feared, now began to cry, and Mason volunteered the opinion that he probably thought 'or pigeons' was one word and didn't know what it meant. I told him that when I wanted his advice I would ask for it, and added that as nearly half the period had already been wasted we should not do mental arithmetic, as I had promised, but instead would refresh our memories of Pythagoras. 'And stop that groaning,' I added sharply.

I had barely completed the construction on the blackboard

when some boy – Mason again, I think – calmly announced, without even troubling to hold up his hand: 'Major Faggott says there's a much easier way of proving it than that – by trigonometry or something.'

I walked to my desk and carefully balanced my chalk on the ledge. 'Is Major Faggott teaching you geometry,' I asked, striving to keep my voice under control, 'or am I?'

'Neither,' said Mason under his breath – but not quietly enough to save the whole set from being kept in for an hour this afternoon.

I attribute the indiscipline with which I had to deal this morning entirely to the influence of Faggott. When one of the staff, however temporary, swaggers about the place setting rules at naught, ridiculing the school customs, smoking in the corridors and (as I actually heard at lunch today) openly admitting his intention of running up to Town to see one of the most *risqué* musical-comedies of the day, how can one expect the boys to remain uncontaminated? The last straw, to me personally, came this afternoon when in the hearing of several quite junior boys, including one new boy, he loudly addressed me as 'The Great Wen' – a punning allusion, presumably, to the first syllable of my name. If it were not for an instinctive dislike of anything that savours of sneaking I should long ago have gone to the Headmaster. That I shall do only as a last resort. Meanwhile, as Gilbert says, there are other ways. . . .

THURSDAY, 9 MARCH

Boys are curious creatures. This morning, apropos of some point that arose in connexion with percentages, Williamson asked whether it was true that schoolmasters were to be exempt from National Service, and I said I believed it was and explained that even in wartime education had to go on. Several boys said it was a swizz (meaning swizzle). Hopgood II then advanced the extraordinary theory that in an emergency everybody who had a moustache would be compelled to shave it off. If Mason or Atkins had made such a statement I should

have come down on them pretty sharply, as I wear a small
moustache myself and have had reason in the past to suspect
both these boys of impertinence (though, to be fair, not actually on that subject), but Hopgood II is a quiet studious boy,
who, as I wrote in his Report last term, is keen on his work and
should do well. So I asked him, with a smile, what would be
the purpose of such an extreme measure, to which he replied
that he thought it had something to do with mustard gas and
that people with moustaches would be more difficult to decon-
taminate than those without. This made Mason and some of
the others laugh so immoderately that I had to call the set to
order.

'That will do,' I said sharply. 'Stranger things than that may
happen in war.'

Etheridge suddenly shouted out 'Beards!' and went very
red when I asked him to explain himself. He apologized and
said he had just realized that Hopgood must mean beards, not
moustaches, because you couldn't get a gas-mask on with a
beard because it had to be rolled up inside and then it choked
you, or anyway you couldn't see clearly through the eyepieces.

'That is as it may be, Etheridge,' I began, 'but we are not
here to discuss whether or not beards can be worn with gas-
masks – .'

'Couldn't they cut a slit in the chin part to let the beard out?'
interrupted Mason rather rudely.

'Say "Sir" if you are speaking to me, Mason,' I reminded
him, but it turned out that he was speaking to Etheridge.

I hoped that this not very edifying discussion was now at an
end, but Williamson, despite a warning frown from me, started
an argument with Mason about the effects of mustard gas on
beards, objecting that if a beard was left hanging outside the
mask it would be destroyed. Mason said he didn't believe it and
anyway it wouldn't matter much if it was, and Hillman then
chipped in with the remark that it was a pity old Mr Poole (our
dear old French master, who retired a year ago) wasn't still
here; they could have put some mustard on his beard and
watched the result.

'He put a good deal on it himself in his time,' Mason said, 'and nothing happened.'

'It grew longer, if anything,' said Atkins.

One of the things every schoolmaster has to learn sooner or later is never to permit, still less to encourage, criticism of his colleagues. Nothing is more fatal to discipline than to appear even for a moment to countenance any lack of respect for another master, whatever one's personal opinions may be (it went against the grain, for instance, to punish Otterway the other day for a remark he made about Major Faggott, but I had to do it); and I certainly did not propose to allow a slighting reference to such a faithful old friend and loyal servant of the school as Mr Poole, just because he was no longer with us. I told them pretty straight that it was cowardly to attack people behind their backs, and I was not going to have it; they would never have dared to suggest putting mustard on Mr Poole's beard if he had been still at Burgrove.

I had forgotten, as a matter of fact, until Mason reminded me of it, that they did actually put salt in the old man's hair one day towards the end of his time here, when he was losing something of his vigour and grip. How it was done remains a mystery. According to one story the salt was sprinkled in his hat; according to another they somehow persuaded poor Poole that it was good for his scalp and put it on with his consent. Yet a third account says that it was not ordinary salt but effervescent, and that the point of the joke (if such it could be called) came when he smoothed down his hair, as was his invariable custom, with a damp brush. But whatever the truth of the matter, it was a cruel prank and nothing, as I told Mason, to laugh about.

'However,' I went on, 'as you all seem so interested in the subject of gas-masks, let me see what you can make of this: In a town of four thousand five hundred inhabitants two hundred and forty of the men were bearded. . . .'

'In Greece,' remarked Sapoulos, 'that would give surprise.'

'How many of the women?' asked Atkins.

I mention these stupid interjections only to observe that a

schoolmaster's success or failure in dealing with young boys depends upon the extent to which he allows himself to be disconcerted or thrown out of his stride by over-eager or ill-timed interruptions. Experience has taught me that to ignore them is often quite sufficient rebuke to the boys concerned. Spoken reproof, except in cases of glaring impertinence or insubordination, is unnecessary and may lead to endless controversy. The golden rule is; Never allow oneself to be side-tracked.

'– what percentage of the population,' I proceeded smoothly, 'would find an ordinary gas-mask difficult or impossible to adjust?'

One or two boys, as usual, wanted the question repeated, but in two or three minutes they were all hard at work. Nothing arouses their keenness so much as a really practical problem to solve, and of course there was the added incentive of ten marks for the first boy to show up the correct answer, nine for the second, and so on. I had hardly had time to jot down the figures myself before Etheridge arrived at my desk to claim the highest mark, followed in quick succession by Hillman, Trench and Williamson. Then Anderson and Atkins had a race, though they know perfectly well that I will not have running or scrapping in the classroom, and ended by knocking over my ink-pot. I whipped open the desk, through the hinge of which the ink was already beginning to pour, and to my dismay found that I had only a small scrap of blotting-paper. The boys helped with what they had, but it was quite insufficient to deal with the situation. There was nothing for it but to send Etheridge off with a note to Major Faggott, who has taken over Rawlinson's duties in charge of the stationery commissariat – loth though I was to ask any favour of the man. I took care to explain the urgency of the case, and so could hardly believe my eyes when Etheridge returned without any blotting-paper but with a brief *unsealed* note from Faggott saying 'Soak it up yourself'.

I put the note in my pocket without a word and went straight along to Faggott's classroom. I found him with his feet up on the desk, reading to the boys, I was quick to notice, from Green's *History of the English People*, though I know for a fact that Rawlinson uses Oman. 'Hallo!' he said, not troubling to alter his position. 'Anything wrong?'

I was boiling with rage but controlled myself in front of the form and simply said that I was sorry to disturb him in any way (with a meaning glance at his feet) but I must have blotting-paper at once, as there had been an accident.

'Well,' he said, 'the cupboard's open.'

I turned on my heel and left the room. It was quite obvious that it never entered his head to come along with me and hand out the blotting-paper himself in the proper manner. Not that I minded fetching it myself, in a way, but that the stationery cupboard should be left like that, *unlocked* on a *Thursday*. . . .

I shall not, of course, allow the matter to rest there.

SUNDAY, 12 MARCH

[*The following entries appear to have been made at different times on the same day: the first, I should say, just before supper, the second, which is not always easy to read and in places, to tell the truth, is downright illegible, later on in the evening.*]

Faggott's last day. He goes, I believe, early tomorrow morning, and I for one shall not be sorry to see the last of him. One learns as a schoolmaster to rub along with all sorts and conditions of men – 'Look for the good qualities not the bad in your colleagues' is a useful motto, generally speaking, for Common Room life – but really, for anyone who cares for the good name of the school and who feels, well, without any snobbishness, that the teaching of young boys is a job better left to gentlemen (in the best sense of the word, of course), I must say that the last fortnight or so has been something of a trial. However, least said, perhaps, soonest mended.

In view of all that has happened I was thunderstruck, to say the least, when Gilbert told me quite casually this afternoon that Faggott proposed to hold a farewell party in his room after supper and hoped I would come along. I thought it typical of the man's monstrous cheek and said so; wild horses, I told him would not drag me to any party of Faggott's – even one which was to celebrate his departure. But Gilbert was most persuasive. After all, he said, the man was going and what was the use of bearing a grudge? 'Besides,' he added with a wink, 'I happen to know that Faggott is going to see the Squid at half-past ten tonight.'

'Steady!' I said, glancing anxiously round to see if any of the boys had heard the disrespectful term. 'They'll be out of the boot-room in a moment. Anyway, what has Faggott's interview with the Headmaster got to do with it?'

'Well,' Gilbert said, 'it has occurred to me that if it's pretty obvious, even to the Reverend Saunders, that Faggott has been celebrating when he goes to see him, there won't be much risk of Faggott getting asked here again, if you see what I mean. You don't want him back, do you? Very well, then, that's why I want you to come. The more there are of us, the merrier he will be. See the point?'

I confess I did not altogether care for Gilbert's suggestion. even if, as I half suspect, he only meant it in fun, but remembering what he had said about not bearing a grudge and so on, I consented to look in at Faggott's party for a few moments. It is to be at eight o'clock, apparently. Supper is at seven here on Sundays.

The Headmaster was bitterly resentful of his attitude. Bitterly. Look at my trousers. My coat and trousers are not what they were not what they were. What will Matron say when she sees my trousers and my coat and trousers? Trousers trousers trousers trousers trowsers? trews rather. *Bracæ*=trews. What will Matron say? It is no business of hers. None at all. My trousers are my own pigeon as I told the Headmaster. I regret his attitude and I told him. Bitterly.

'WHO PUT THAT PIGEON IN MY TROUSERS?'

Never mind the pigeon now, Wentworth, Esq., B.A. Let me tell the story in my own way. I went to Faggott's room and Collingridge and Gilbert and Rawlinson has been ill but there he was. I am Senior Mathmatics master at Burgrove Preparatory School and I went to Faggott's room. Mathmatics mathematics. Who put the 'e' in mathematics? Stand up the boy who put the 'e' in mathematics. I have been at Burgrove for seven years and in all my seven years at Burgrove I have never had such a thing happen. Never. The long and short of it is that Gilbert was in Faggott's room and Faggott was there and we all sang. I had a whisky and Faggott sang. I like Faggott and I had a whisky because he is going away. Mind you, there was a time when things were different. Not the same. But now they are the same all right and I like Faggott. Then he sang again and I had another whisky because I like him. While he was singing I told him so. 'I bear no grudge,' I said, and he was pleased. Then we all had whiskies and I sang. We all sang. They all sang. He was about to have sung. *Cano – canare.* CANARY! See the point, Mason? *cano* – canary – cantuar. The Archbishop of Canterbury sang!

I fell in a puddle and tore my trousers. The fact of the matter is that Faggott was drunk. Faggott was drunk when he went to see the Headmaster and I ran after him to stop him. Good old Faggott. They tried to prevent me but I ran after him and fell into a puddle in the dark and tore my trousers. So I did not catch him until he reached the Headmaster's door. I seized his coat-tails as he was going in and he lost his balance and fell, but he did not tear his trousers. I am certain of that. He simply fell backwards on the floor and lay there while I spoke to the Headmaster. I went straight up to the Headmaster and took him by the lapels. 'I bear no grudge, Headmaster,' I said. He did not seem to understand, so I showed him the state of my trousers and asked him what in the world he thought Matron would have to say about them. Then Faggott pushed me aside. I was upset and began to sing 'Asleep in the Deep'. Anybody would. But after a while the Headmaster came up and told me to go back to my room at once and get to bed. He said that unless such a thing ever happened again he would say no more about it. He will regret that. I pointed out that I was Senior Mathematics master at Burgrove Preparatory School, which was true. But his attitude was contumacious. I told him his attitude was contumelious. Then I said good night, as I had done all I could for Faggott for the time being.

When I had got out of the room I remembered something and
went back.

'It's about my trousers, Headmaster,' I said. That is what
I resent so bitterly. I have done my best and the Headmaster's
attitude is contumelious, as I told him. Afterwards . . .

# Summer Term 1939
## Prelude to Disaster

Nothing, I suppose, can now stop the story getting about. I blame the Headmaster for this. Had he listened quietly to my explanation, as I think I had a right to expect, instead of wilfully misinterpreting the situation in which he chanced to find me, the whole ridiculous affair would have been cleared up, my coat would have been on and the fishing-rod back in its place long before Wilson and Tremayne peeped into the bootroom. As it is, goodness knows what wild rumours the boys will spread about the incident. Already some young ass has chalked 'LOBSTER POTS. KEEP OFF' on the top of the bootlockers; the next thing I suppose will be ground-bait on the floor of my form-room and similar follies. Well, I shall know how to deal with that kind of humour.

Looking back I cannot see that I acted unwisely at any point, given the unusual circumstances in which I found myself. If the Headmaster cannot understand why I should want my umbrella at eleven o'clock at night, it shows a want of sensibility on his part, not any lack of sense on mine. The fact is that I did *not* want my umbrella, in one way, for it was a fine starlight night and I had nowhere to go – unless it had occured to me to go for a walk at that improbable hour of night – which I should never have done had it been raining, naturally. I simply wanted to know where my umbrella was.

I had expected it to be down at the cottage, actually, but noticing quite by chance that it was not in its usual corner in the hall I had a hunt in my bedroom and still failed to find it. I became rather worried and as it was a fine night decided to set my mind at rest by strolling up to the school and having a look in the Common Room cupboard – not the cupboard *in* the Common Room, where we keep our gowns, but the tall one just outside where cricket bats and so on are kept in the winter and footballs in the summer. What the Headmaster cannot seem to see is that it was only *because* it was a fine night that I was looking for it at all. It would have been madness to walk up to School through a downpour simply to see whether my umbrella was there or not.

At any rate I went straight to the cupboard, not troubling to switch on the lights for I had my torch with me, and had just ascertained that my umbrella was *not* there when I stepped back on to a cricket ball, and, in saving myself from a tumble, had the ill-fortune to smash my torch against the wall. So I had to grope my way out of the cupboard in the dark and in doing so dislodged Gilbert's fishing-rod which fell with a clatter to the floor. Rather carelessly, in my opinion, though I am no fisherman, he keeps it set up ready for an occasional afternoon with the grayling, instead of taking it to pieces when he has finished with it. Luckily I found the rod after a little trouble, by sweeping about with my hands, and stood it up again in its corner. Then I turned to go out, but to my astonishment as I moved the rod fell down again. When the same thing happened a third time I decided to leave the rod where it was until I had put the lights on and could see what the trouble was. I had not yet realized of course what had happened. But the moment I took a step into the corridor I felt something pluck sharply at my clothing at the back and a kind of grating scream came out of the depths of the cupboard. I am not easily rattled – I should hardly be a schoolmaster if I were – but I confess that for a moment my blood ran cold. Then I pulled myself together, put my hand behind my back and grasped the gut that was holding me fast to Gilbert's rod and reel.

By ill-chance the hook had caught me firmly between the shoulder blades, out of reach, and though I might have broken the gut I did not care, except as a last resort, deliberately to damage a colleague's property. I was now in something of a dilemma. Had it been merely a question of getting to the light-switch in the corridor the problem would have been relatively simple; but it was not, for all downstairs lights in the school buildings are controlled by a master-switch behind the boot-room door, and this the Headmaster himself switches off every evening at half-past ten. It was out of the question to attempt to make my way to the boot-room with the reel screaming behind me at every step. I should have woken every boy in the house. I therefore decided, as I think rightly, to take the rod with me to the boot-room (carrying it of course in my hand). To avoid further noise I re-entered the cupboard backwards on my hands and knees, or rather on my knees and right hand, for with my left I kept contact with the line. In this way I had no difficulty in finding the tip of the rod. Then working my fingers down until I grasped the butt I rose to my feet and left the cupboard for the last time.

It was no easy journey to the boot-room. If I raised the point of the rod too high the result was a sharp tug at my shoulders and a warning scream from the reel, while to lower it too much was to run the risk of entanglement in the slack. It was, I suppose, fear of this latter disaster that made me raise the point too sharply after manoeuvring it carefully through the boot-room door. Unknown to me, the line at the very tip of the rod looped itself round the hasp of the fan-light over the door, and inevitably at my next step forward the coat rose on my back, the rod quivered in my hands and a yard of line was stripped with great violence from the reel.

There was now only one thing to be done. I leaned the rod against the door-jamb, removed my coat and lowered it with great care to the floor, at the same time keeping one hand on the rod in case it should be pulled over by the movement of the coat. I was now of course free and very soon had the master-switch down and the boot-room light working. Then I picked up the rod and, stepping on to the boot-lockers, lifted the line clear of the fan-light hasp.

That the Head should appear at this moment was only in keeping, I suppose, with the miserable ill-fortune I had met with all through.

'Ah, Wentworth,' he said. 'I thought I heard a noise.' Then his eyebrows went up.

'Do you often come here to fish?' he asked.

'I was worried about my umbrella, sir,' I began, realizing at once that until he knew what had happened my behaviour must seem very odd, 'and as it is a fine night – ' but he cut my explanation short.

'I see,' he said. 'And you thought a little fishing would take your mind off your worries? You have foul-hooked your coat, I notice.'

'This rod was in the Common Room cupboard, Head-master,' I explained, stepping down off the lockers, 'and as you can see, the hook caught my coat while I was looking for my umbrella. It is Gilbert's rod,' 1 added.

The Headmaster still looked dubious. 'It's a long cast from the cupboard to the boot-room, Wentworth,' he objected.

'My coat was in the cupboard, sir,' I said with some impatience. 'If you would allow me to explain the whole thing – '

'No, no,' he said. 'No. I don't wish to pry into my masters' affairs. I have no objection whatever to your fishing in the cupboard, provided the boys are not disturbed. But I do think it ought to stop there. I *cannot* understand how you come to be in your shirt-sleeves in the boot-room, considering – What do *you* want?'

He had turned sharply, and to my dismay I caught a glimpse over his shoulder of Wilson and Tremayne in their dressing-gowns.

'I – we're sorry, sir,' said Tremayne, looking at my fishing-rod with his eyes popping out of his head. 'I didn't know – we thought we heard a queer noise – '

'Get off to bed, both of you, at once,' ordered the Head-master, and when they had run off, he turned back to me and made the most inexplicable remark.

'You and your umbrella, Wentworth,' he said. 'You'll be the death of me yet.'

What is particularly puzzling is that this is the first occasion, so far as I know, on which I have even mentioned my umbrella to the Headmaster.

WEDNESDAY, 17 MAY

'A train,' I read out to my IIIA boys, 'leaves Edinburgh for
Glasgow at half-past three, arriving at its destination – Well,
what *is* it, Etheridge?'

I understood him to say that the half-past three from Edinburgh now left at quarter to four, or some such rubbish.

'Are you trying to be funny?' I demanded sternly.

I think he was genuinely surprised by my attitude, for he
flushed up to the roots of his hair and answered quite seriously,
'Good lord, no, sir. It's the summer time-tables, sir. They've
put the three-thirty Glasgow train back fifteen minutes so as to
connect with the one-fifty two – '

'Etheridge lives in Edinburgh, sir,' explained Mason in his
interfering way.

'He's nuts on *Bradshaw*, too,' added Atkins. 'I'll bet he's
right, sir.'

I thanked them all for their assistance, and pointed out that
for the purposes of the problem I was about to ask them to be
good enough to undertake, it was really immaterial whether
Etheridge lived in Edinburgh or Clacton-on-Sea. 'Nor,' I
added to clinch the matter, 'do I care a brass farthing if
*Bradshaw* says the half-past three train starts at breakfast-time.
*I'm* not "nuts on *Bradshaw*", Atkins.'

'I only thought we might as well have it right, sir,' said
Etheridge.

'Can't you see, you little nanny-goat,' I cried in exasperation, 'that we are not concerned with what actually happens
*now*! I am giving out a sum, not arranging a Sunday outing
on the Clyde.'

'Oh, Sunday?' Etheridge said. 'She doesn't run on Sundays.'

'I see,' I said ironically; 'she doesn't run on Sundays. Well,
if everybody has made a note of that important fact, perhaps
we can get on with our work. Doesn't run on Sundays, indeed!
We shall have Mason asking for a non-smoker, next.'

When the laughter raised by this sally had died down I gave
them the remaining details of the problem, namely that the
three-thirty arrives in Glasgow at five o'clock whereas a train

leaving Glasgow at the same time reaches Edinburgh in exactly two hours. The distance between the two places is given as sixty miles (Etheridge opened his silly mouth at this, but I quietened him with a frown), and the problem is of course to discover at what distance from Edinburgh the two trains meet.

I had hardly finished speaking before Williamson, rather an obtuse boy, began to protest that they couldn't do that without knowing the speed of the trains.

'*Think*, boy,' I implored him. 'How far apart are the two stations? Sixty miles? Right, and how long does the train from Glasgow to Edinburgh take? Two hours, doesn't it? Very well, then. Now, can you tell me the speed in miles per hour?'

'No, sir.'

'No, Williamson?'

'No, sir. At least – no, sir, not unless I know how often the train stops.'

'There are no stops whatever, Williamson,' I told him wearily. 'You can take it that the train is an express.'

'Sixty miles in two hours!' cried Mason. 'Golly, what a flier!'

'Get on, Mason,' I said sharply. 'All right now, Williamson?'

'I think so, thank you, sir. Except what about the other train, the one going from Edinburgh, the three-thirty, sir?'

'They're both three-thirties, fool,' said somebody, but though I whipped round like a flash I wasn't quick enough to catch him.

'What about it?' I asked, returning to Williamson.

'I mean, does it stop?'

'It stops at Airdrie,' put in Etheridge before I could speak. 'If you mean the three-forty-five, that is.'

'In here at two-thirty sharp, Etheridge,' I ordered, losing patience. 'And you too, Mason, if you can't stop that idiotic grinning. We are wasting far too much time. Both trains – you'd better listen to this all of you, because I'm not going to answer any more questions – both trains are expresses and run at a constant speed from start to finish.'

'In that case, sir,' objected Atkins, 'I don't see why one of them gets there first.'

'Tell him, somebody.'

'Because it's got farther to go,' suggested Williamson.

'Oh, jolly good, Batty!' one of them shouted, and not being able to think of a better comment myself I let it pass.

Shortly after this I left the form-room for a moment, ostensibly to fetch a book from the Common Rom, but in reality to stop the boys asking questions and force them to work the difficulties out for themselves. In the corridor I met the Headmaster.

'Hullo, Wentworth,' he greeted me, taking my elbow. 'I've been wanting a word with you. You never told me the real history of that fishing trip of yours the other night. I'm dying to know.'

'As I think I told you in the boot-room at the time, Headmaster,' I began stiffly, 'I was merely looking for my umbrella – '

'*Because* it was a fine night.'

'Exactly. And as – '

'Did you find it?'

'No,' I said. 'Unfortunately not. It was extremely dark in the cupboard as you can imagine – '

'And you took Gilbert's rod by mistake? I see.'

'There was no mistake about it, Headmaster,' I said warmly. 'I may be all kinds of a fool, but I can still distinguish between my umbrella and a nine-foot fishing-rod, I am thankful to say.'

'Then you took the rod to the boot-room on purpose?'

'The point is,' I explained, 'that I could not leave the cupboard without it. So, rather than spend the whole night in the cupboard, I took it with me.'

'Remember, a term or two ago, how you took a maidenhair fern out of my study, Wentworth? I thought at the time it was some sort of uncontrollable impulse that came over you, and I suppose this – this sudden desire to fish comes in the same category, eh?'

But for a twinkle in the Headmaster's eye I should have been seriously annoyed at this reference to a silly misunderstanding that once occurred over a pot-plant of his. Not that the plant was of any particular value to me or anyone else, as it happened.

'If you would let me show you exactly what happened, Headmaster?' I suggested.

He turned away and stood with his back to me for a while, looking out over the playing fields.

'You mean,' he said at last, turning round with an expression I could not quite fathom, 'you mean – go in the cupboard again?'

I nodded, and he at once agreed to come and watch my demonstration after lunch.

'Half-past two, Wentworth,' he said, adding rather inconsequently, 'I'll send the School out for a walk.'

Thinking it over, I am not sure that I have been wise; I doubt whether any good will come of it. For one thing, of course, I have had to let Mason and Etheridge off detention.

## WENTWORTH RE-ENTERS THE CUPBOARD

[*I am indebted to Mr Charles Gilbert for the following account of what took place that afternoon. Mr Wentworth himself is silent on the point.*]

Anybody who has known Wentworth for more than a couple of minutes is aware that however much of a clown he makes of himself, whatever fantastic predicament he gets into, he will not leave the thing alone. He will not rest until he has proved to his own satisfaction, and attempted to convince everybody else, that the whole affair was perfectly natural really. If he was found hanging by his braces from the dome of St Paul's (and nobody here would be the least surprised if he were) he would put it down to negligence on the part of the Dean, coupled with a certain amount of sheer bad luck on his own part. 'In attempting,' he would say, 'to make my way out of the Whispering Gallery I had the misfortune to catch my foot. . . .'

Undoubtedly it was this feeling that led Wentworth to give a demonstration to the Headmaster of the way in which he got snared in my fishing-line, and to show how inevitably this mischance compelled him to climb on to the lockers in the boot-room, with my rod in his hand, and his coat, firmly hooked, gasping out its life on the floor.

Rawlinson and I knew nothing about this demonstration, as a matter of fact, until just before it was due to begin. We happened to be talking to Wentworth, who was hanging about outside the cupboard by the Common Room door, when the Headmaster came along.

'Ah, Wentworth,' he said. 'I see you've got quite a gathering for it.'

'Gilbert and Rawlinson are just off for a walk, sir,' Wentworth explained.

'No hurry,' I said, 'if we can be of any use.'

'Well, Gilbert,' old Saunders said, 'you ought to be present, as it was your rod,' and he explained, not without a certain difficulty in controlling his voice, what Wentworth was going to do.

So we saw the whole thing.

Wentworth began with a long rigmarole, which I cannot attempt to follow in detail, about his umbrella. The upshot of it seemed to be that as he didn't want it the sensible thing to do was to come up in the dark and look for it in the games cupboard. Asked by Rawlinson whether he kept his umbrella in the games cupboard, he said, 'Of course not,' which settled that point. Then he went into the cupboard, still talking.

'You can imagine, Headmaster, that when I lost the use of my torch it was pitch dark in here. It is pretty dark in here now, even by day, as you can see.'

We all crowded into the cupboard after him, to see just how dark it was, and Rawlinson, with a stroke of genius, shut the door 'in order to reproduce as closely as possible the actual conditions'. It was now very dark indeed, and we were jammed so tightly together that I could distinctly feel old Saunders shaking all over with suppressed laughter. I was, as a matter of fact, shaking myself.

'What did you do then, Wentworth?'

'My first thought naturally, Headmaster, was to get some light, and I therefore made my way – I beg your pardon, sir.'

'It's all right,' said Rawlinson, 'that was *my* foot.'

'If we could have a little light – Ah! What's this?' There was a slight clatter and almost simultaneously I was butted violently by Wentworth, who appeared to be sweeping the floor with his hands.

'Let go my leg,' cried the Headmaster suddenly, and immediately burst into uncontrollable laughter. Only Wentworth was still able to speak and he, in rather a querulous voice, kept asking why somebody didn't open the door.

Somebody did, from the outside, and we heard the indignant voice of Miss Coombes (our music lady) demanding 'What are you boys doing in there? Come out at once!'

I doubt if a more sheepish lot ever trailed out of a cupboard than the Headmaster and staff of Burgrove Preparatory School.

'Why, Mr Saunders!' she cried. 'I – I'm sorry to – to have interrupted you, but I thought perhaps – '

It was an awkward little scene. Only Wentworth, who has been through too much, I suppose, to be concerned about a straightforward situation like this, looked altogether at ease.

'I've got it, you see, Miss Coombes,' he said, flourishing his umbrella. 'I had an idea it might be in there, all along.'

When Miss Coombes had left us, very red in the face, the Headmaster rounded on Wentworth.

'So that's what you had round my ankle, you old rascal. You would have had me over, if there had been any room to fall down in.'

Wentworth pointed out gravely that there had of course been more room on the night he had first looked for his umbrella. 'I was by myself, you see,' he explained, and we agreed that this was just as well.

The rest of the demonstration went off almost without a hitch. We got him hooked up, as directed, and off he went with a March Brown firmly anchored in his coat at the back and my rod clasped in his right hand – exactly as on the night, except that he was not on that occasion carrying his umbrella as well.

He showed us how, on entering the boot-room in search of the light-switch, he had raised the point of the rod too high and so, 'as ill-luck would have it', got the top of the line looped round the hasp on the fan-light. He had first become aware of this, 'you will understand, Headmaster,' when he felt a jerk and heard more line screaming off the reel; and he demonstrated the jerk and the scream most convincingly. But he failed to notice, and we felt it unnecessary to point out, that on this occasion the reel had overrun, so that a loop of slack line was left hanging between the reel and the first eye on the rod.

I need hardly say that Wentworth put his foot through this loop. It is a fairly easy thing to do, but nobody could have done it more easily than he did.

'Hullo!' he said. 'I'm caught.'

'Did this happen when – on the night?' we asked.

'No. Oh, no,' he said, smiling. 'This is an unrehearsed effect.'

He was standing on one leg now, trying to scrape the line off his right calf with the point of his umbrella. When he began to lose his balance I had a moment's uneasiness, for I feared he might put his right foot down too abruptly, trying to save himself, and thereby snap the point of the rod. But I need not have worried. With the umbrella between his legs he never had a chance, and after spinning right round twice like a top he had to confess himself beaten and went down with all hands into the boot-basket.

'Are you hurt, old chap?' I asked, as soon as I could speak.

'No, no,' he said, struggling to get up. 'I am all right, thank you. But I am worried about my umbrella.'

'You said that the first time,' cried the Headmaster, and rushed off hooting, I regret to say, like a madman.

We could hear him, far off down the corridor, beating his knees with his hands and repeating at intervals with a kind of incredulous awe, 'He's worried about his umbrella! Oh, my aunt, he's *still* worried about his umbrella!'

FRIDAY, 23 JUNE – EVE OF FOUNDATION DAY

I felt tired and depressed when I woke up today. The depression lasted all morning and I found it difficult to concentrate on my work, with the result that in working out a sum concerning the price of eggs my mind wandered to the wall-papering problems which we did last week. This led me to attempt to find the perimeter of the eggs in feet and inches, which of course, not knowing the measurement of the eggs, I could not do. I rubbed it all out and began again but was still muddled and got an answer giving the number of eggs (which of course we knew already) instead of their price. Very unwillingly, for I dislike anything that savours of subterfuge, I explained to the boys that I had done this in order to test them and called Mason up to point out where I had gone wrong. He said that he couldn't see anything wrong with it except that it was a mistake to try to paper a room with eggs – at which we all laughed. He asked for a mark, which I allowed, perhaps unjustifiably, but I was in no mood for argument, and I offered to double it if he could work out the sum correctly himself. He said, 'Let $x$ be an egg.'

I told Etheridge to stop tittering and nodded to Mason.

'Well, sir, then twelve eggs equal $12x$.'

'Well?'

'Then 94 eggs equal $12x$ multiplied by 94 over 12, that's to say, sir – er – 94 eggs equal – um – $94x$.'

'I see,' I said. 'So 94 eggs equal $94x$. Go on.'

'So, you see, sir, as 94 eggs cost ten shillings therefore $94x$ equals ten. Then if the price goes up a halfpenny a dozen, the cost of a gross – at least, wait a minute, sir, if 94 eggs equal $94x$ then surely $x$ equals one?'

'One what?'

'One egg, sir.'

I threw up my hands. 'What on earth is the good of that, Mason?' I asked.

The boy looked genuinely surprised. 'That's the value of $x$, sir. I thought that's what you wanted.'

'Do you mean to say that that is your answer?'

He said it was, and when I told him to sit down, calmly asked for another mark. It is this kind of attitude that makes a schoolmaster's task so unnecessarily difficult and wearing. Boys like Mason make no attempt to get to the root of a problem, they simply let $x$ equal anything that occurs to them, whether it has any bearing on the sum or not, and imagine that by multiplying and dividing it they will arrive at some sort of answer and perhaps get a mark for their trouble. Naturally it is particularly annoying to find them using $x$ in a sum of this kind which does not call for the introduction of an unknown quantity. I worked the problem out again myself, getting it right this time – only to find Hillman drawing horses on his blotting-paper (a silly trick) and Hopgood II asleep. There is something wrong with Hopgood II, I think, but whenever I speak to Matron about his drowsiness she merely says that none of the other masters have complained of his going to sleep in their forms. As if that had anything to do with it.

After dinner this evening I went to see the Head on some small point about Common Entrance papers, forgetting that tomorrow is Foundation Day here and that the Bishop of Saintsbury, who has kindly consented to preach at the morning service, would naturally be staying the night. However, the Headmaster made me welcome, cutting short my attempted explanations with a genial 'No shop now, Wentworth!' and invited me to take coffee with them. I accepted and we had a pleasant chat.

The Bishop seems to be a man with wide interests, not at all 'churchy' or wrapped up in narrow diocesan affairs. He was talking about the Bren gun when I came in and good-naturedly included me in the conversation by asking whether I could tell him the average life of the barrel. I said I had no idea, and asked him in my turn whether he by any chance knew a Canon Slinford, who had, I believed, or used to have, associations with Saintsbury. He said he did not, but he knew, of course, Lady Slinford, the niece of the Earl of Belsize, who had recently married one of the Worcestershire Frumps – or some such name. I replied with a smile that so far as I knew the Canon was not connected with any noble family, whereupon he turned to the Headmaster and began to talk to him about Swedish pom-poms – all Greek to me. Apparently the Bishop had been dining recently with a member of the Cabinet who told him in confidence that their manufacture was going ahead by leaps and bounds. Then the conversation turned to tanks.

Mr Saunders ventured to observe that he supposed the day of
the horse in warfare was over, but with this the Bishop could
not altogether agree.

Hearing the horse mentioned and not wishing to be left out
of the conversation, I quoted the first apposite line from the
Bible which came into my head, 'The glory of his nostrils is
terrible.'

'Whom do you mean, sir?' asked the Bishop, wheeling
round.

I explained that I meant the horse and added 'Ha Ha
among the trumpets' to make the reference clear. Our visitor
replied with a grunt and seeing that he was becoming tired,
not unnaturally, of this rather military talk, I put a question
to him about his diocese, which I had always understood to be
largely agricultural and therefore at the moment going,
perhaps, through a rather difficult time. But he misunderstood
my meaning, replying that the chief trouble was a serious
shortage of ambulance drivers and quoting figures which
seemed to relate, so far as I could follow them, to the Auxiliary
Fire Brigade. This talking at cross-purposes confused me and
I said good night and took my leave without remembering to
ask, as I had intended, about the Lessons for tomorrow. Presumably the Headmaster will read the second, leaving 'Let us
now praise famous men' to me, in the ordinary way, but it is
just possible he may wish to spare his voice, in view of his
Speech, and in that case Rawlinson should, I suppose, be
warned. I returned to the study to make sure, but finding the
Bishop on the floor expounding some point in connexion with
high-angle fire, crept out again without disturbing him.

It is all rather puzzling. But no doubt everything will go off
splendidly tomorrow.

SATURDAY, 24 JUNE – FOUNDATION DAY

And what a day it has been! No school, of course, but a great
deal to arrange and the prizes to see to, and so on. It wouldn't
do to have any hitch at the last moment with all the parents in
their places and our whole organization *sub judice* so to speak,
or whatever the expression is. There *was* a bit of a difficulty, as

a matter of fact, because the wrong *Decline and Fall* had been sent – nothing to do with the Roman Empire as far as I could see on a hasty inspection, and in places hardly suitable for young boys. When I pointed this out to the Headmaster immediately after breakfast, he laughed and said it was lucky they hadn't sent the right one or we should never have got it all into the gym (where we have the prize-giving nowadays).

'But what are we to do, Headmaster?' I asked. 'Baylis will be terribly disappointed if there is no prize for him.'

He said he was very busy and had every confidence in my ability to do what seemed best – all very well, but I cannot be expected to conjure books out of thin air, especially on a day like this when I have enough to do in all conscience and the whole place is swarming with parents determined to get hold of one and talk about their boys. However, I managed to find Thring, whose parents are in India, and arranged that after receiving his copy of *Ivanhoe* he should hand it at once to one of the senior boys who would unobtrusively return it to the table. It could then be presented again to Baylis when his turn came and nobody need be any the wiser. Of course I promised that Thring should have another copy as soon as it could be obtained. He asked if he might have *Forty Years Under the Sea*, or some such book, instead. I had never heard of it and doubted whether it would have the same appeal for a boy as *Ivanhoe*, so I gave a non-committal reply. I don't see that I could have made any better arrangement on the spur of the moment.

Just before Chapel I met the Bishop taking a stroll down the Avenue and put some casual question to him about Consistory Courts, merely as a means of opening a conversation. To my astonishment he burst into a torrent of what I should have described, in one not of his cloth, as angry abuse, asking me what the dickens I thought I was playing at, whether I imagined he was the Archbishop of Canterbury in disguise or what, and a lot more incomprehensible questions. 'But surely,' I said, 'you are the Bishop of Saintsbury?'

It turns out that he is not a Bishop at all, but a retired Colonel who has taken Orders late in life 'for want,' as he chose to put it, 'of something better to do.' How Gilbert, who definitely told me that the Bishop of Saintsbury was coming down to preach on Foundation Day, came to make the mistake I do not pretend to know. Naturally when I called on the Headmaster last night and discovered a gentleman in clerical dress in his study I took it for granted that his guest was the Bishop. It is true I might have paused to wonder why he was not in apron and gaiters, but the fact of the matter is I simply failed to notice. After all it is no business of mine what bishops wear. I have enough to worry about already without that.

'Why then, Colonel,' I said, after begging his pardon for mistaking him for a Bishop (an error which seemed to fill him with quite unreasonable resentment), 'I wonder if, in your professional capacity, you ever came across a Major Faggott, who was on the staff here a short while ago?'

'Faggott?' he said, 'Faggott? No, never heard of him. Not one of ours, anyway.'

'Whose?' I asked.

'Ours.'

'Oh!' I said, rather at a loss. 'Not one of ours either, really.'

This for some reason made the Colonel think I was an old Army man myself, and after a few minutes' rather fruitless conversation we parted. His sermon, which took the form of an appeal to us all to join the Territorial Army, was rather wasted on the boys, who have all made up their minds to become Air Cadets as soon as they are old enough. Still, he is of course an Old Boy, and we were all glad he was able to come.

I thought the Headmaster's speech went better than ever this year. The parents were obviously pleased at his reference to the health of the school, which, apart from influenza and the mumps epidemic last term, has been uniformly excellent, and they clapped very heartily at the announcement of special Rhythmic Exercise classes in the near future for boys who wish to take them. In games, the Headmaster said, the school had not perhaps been quite so successful as in some previous years, but the general level of performance throughout the school had never, he thought, been higher, and that, after all, was of more importance than the possession of a few boys of outstanding ability in the First Elevens. Turning to work he explained that with an unusually young Sixth Form the Honours List was necessarily a short one; they would all be getting their scholarships next year. But he had much pleasure in congratulating Thomas on his successful entry into the Royal Naval College, Dartmouth. In conclusion he very kindly mentioned the unfailing assistance and loyal support he had received from every member of the Staff.

Afterwards Lady Portcullis gave away the prizes. Hillman, I was glad to see, got the Tidiest Dormitory Prize in his capacity as Aedile of the Junior Green. Aediles, of course, have not the authority of full Praetors (of which there are six), but are put in charge of the smaller dormitories such as the Junior Green, Admiral Benbow and Upper Far – which used to be called Eastman's until the tragedy. There was, after all, a muddle about Baylis's prize, because Thring, apparently misunderstanding my instructions, handed his *Ivanhoe* to Baylis, who was sitting near him, directly he returned to his seat. Then Baylis, when his name was called out by the Headmaster, took the book up with him and gave it back to Lady Portcullis. This naturally confused Lady Portcullis who had just been handed *The Lays of Ancient Rome* (intended as a matter of fact for Thomas) by the Headmaster and, no doubt in order to cover up a moment's hesitation, she asked the boy, very kindly, what his name was. He said it was Thomas, meaning his Christian name, of course (he is quite a little chap really – only nine), and she thereupon gave him *The Lays*, at the same time congratulating him in a clear voice on passing into the Navy. Baylis got very red, but wisely said nothing. This left *Ivanhoe* for Thomas – I mean Thomas, R., of the Upper IV – as his prize for passing the Dartmouth Entrance. He accepted it without comment, though I happen to know that he received a copy of the same novel last term for his work in Set I. Still, there was nothing else to be done.

On the whole a most successful Speech and Prize-giving.

The Old Boys beat the School by three wickets this afternoon.

An excellent game, though I confess my attention was rather distracted at times. Several parents came up to discuss their sons' progress, and in particular I had a long talk with Mrs Hillman. She is petite with blue eyes and is rather charming though a little unorthodox. We talked about ballet for a while, of which I know nothing, and then she suddenly turned to me and remarked, 'What a funny old stick your headmaster is!' I was naturally taken aback, especially as other parents and their boys were standing quite close to us, and I hurriedly observed that I hoped she would be at the concert in the evening. But she refused to take the hint.

'Come now, Mr Wentworth,' she said, laying her small hand on my arm, 'you can't deny it. Look at him talking to that woman in the wig over there.'

'Really, Mrs Hillman!' I said in a low voice. 'We are not alone.'

'That isn't my fault, is it, Mr Wentworth?' she replied.

I was absolutely dumbfounded, and before I could collect my wits she went on in the most confiding way, 'Is he or is he not a pompous old thing?'

'Well – ' I began, and we both laughed.

We soon became firm friends and she talked in a most interesting way about several of the parents, many of whom she seemed to know personally. I pointed out Clarke's mother, a very striking figure in red, and she remarked, 'It costs that woman eight hundred a year to look like that.'

'No one would say that of you, Mrs Hillman,' I said gallantly.

'Meaning that I'm obviously cheaply turned-out?' she replied mischievously.

I simply gave her a look and she lowered her eyes.

'Here comes that spiteful old cat with the wig,' she said presently. 'Now watch. Hullo, Peggy. You know Mr Wentworth, don't you? Mr Wentworth – Lady Cleethorpes.'

'How do you do,' I said.

'We were just talking about you,' said Mrs Hillman. 'Mr Wentworth was saying you looked a spiteful old cat.'

'I assure you, Lady Cleethorpes!' I cried, reddening to the roots of my hair. 'Mrs Hillman is utterly – '

'Did she tell you I wear a wig?'

'I – that is,' I began, completely at a loss for words, 'I should never have guessed – '

'Well, I don't,' said Lady Cleethorpes, and both women went off into peals of laughter.

I felt extremely uncomfortable. People were looking at us – and no wonder. The cricket field, when a serious game is in progress, is not the place for loud laughter. Besides, the whole position was most embarrassing. There seemed to be no knowing what these extraordinary ladies would say next. I determined to bring the conversation back to a sensible level at once.

'How is your husband, Mrs Hillman?' I asked, giving her a reproachful look.

She became serious at once. 'I have no husband – now, Mr Wentworth,' she said.

I murmured a few conventional words of sympathy, cursing myself silently for a clumsy fool, but she cut me short.

'I divorced him,' she said briskly. 'He was no loss.'

'So go in and win, Mr Wentworth,' added Lady Cleethorpes with another of her penetrating laughs.

I may be old-fashioned but I confess I have no use whatever for this kind of talk. Divorce is not a subject for jesting. No doubt, in the world in which some people live, the so-called *haut monde*, it is considered clever and amusing to make light of serious and intimate subjects of this kind, but here at Burgrove we prefer to take a different attitude. Moreover I do not care to be made the object of remarks in, to say the least, doubtful taste, particularly when these involve the good name of a lady who happens to be present.

I made my excuses rather coldly and turned away, not knowing that one of my sock-suspenders had unluckily come unfastened and was trailing on the ground. I might not have noticed had not Mrs Hillman unwittingly set her foot on the metal clasp or fastener so that I was brought up short after a single stride and all but overbalanced. Mrs Hillman very kindly moved her foot in a quite natural way when she noticed my predicament, as if unaware that anything unusual had happened, but Lady Cleethorpes, who seems to be utterly lacking in tact, broke out into another loud laugh and cried, 'You'll have to marry her now.' This was too much for my temper and I fear I might have spoken very sharply to Lady Cleethorpes had not the Headmaster come up at that moment and joined the group.

'Ah!' he said, rubbing his hands together in a way which I am bound to say I sometimes find rather irritating, 'I hope Mr Wentworth has been entertaining you two ladies.'

'He certainly has,' said Lady Cleethorpes.

I left them as soon as I could and wandered off to the far side of the field, where I did my best to forget my annoyance by concentrating on the game. The Old Boys had got to within twenty-five of our total for the loss of four wickets, mainly through Felpman (a mainstay of the Eleven in the old days, though a poor mathematician. Percentages always used to beat him, I remember), and things looked bad for Burgrove. Then Clarke stopped a hot one at extra cover and I joined in the general shouts of 'Play up, School!' Nothing came of it, however.

'Oh, Mr Wentworth,' said a well-known voice, and I turned to find Mrs Hillman at my side. 'I am so sorry,' she said, 'if Peggy annoyed you.'

'It was nothing,' I said stiffly. 'Lady Cleethorpes has perhaps a rather – unusual sense of humour.'

'You're not angry with me, are you?'

I looked down at her kindly, and found to my intense mortification that I was still holding the lose suspender in my right hand. Mrs Hillman followed the direction of my eyes and then, with a discretion that I admired, turned her head away. I stuffed the offending article into my pocket.

'Tell me, Mrs Hillman,' I said, to cover our mutual embarrassment; 'your friend – Lady Cleethorpes – she has no boy here surely? There is no Cleethorpes on the School List. A nephew perhaps?'

'Oh, didn't you know?' she replied, opening her eyes wide in astonishment. 'That's her son over there – that tall good-

looking boy in spectacles. She used to be a Mrs Mason before
her second marriage, you know.'

'*Mason?*' I cried.

'Yes. Johnny Mason. You must know him.'

'Ah!' I said. 'Yes. Yes, yes. Mason! I see.'

[*Two weeks later occurred the unfortunate affair of Hopgood
II and the algebra book which might have had serious consequences for Wentworth's career but for the general amnesty
which a world war brings in its train. Early in 1940 he joined
the army. A few scattered extracts from the diary of Second-
Lieut. Wentworth, R.A. will be found in the next section of
this book.*]

# An Assistant Master at War

I fell over that coil of rubber tubing again this morning on my way back after inspecting the cookhouse and went straight off and reported it to the Adjutant. The thing is simply a death-trap where it is at present. He said, 'Get it moved, then. You're Orderly Officer at this R.H.Q., aren't you?'

I pointed out that I should hardly care to move a piece of equipment without his authority, but that if he gave that authority I would have it moved at once.

'All right,' he said, 'go ahead and move it. And for goodness' sake, Wentworth, don't come and bother me about every trivial thing that crops up. I'm busy.'

I thought this unfair. It is very difficult for a new officer to know just what he may or may not do without reference to higher authority. I determined to get things clear in my mind once for all.

'May I take it then, sir,' I asked, 'that in future I have authority to move such things as coils of tubing and so on without applying to you?'

'Yes, yes, yes,' he said.

'What about benches and tables?'

'Do you want to move benches and tables, Wentworth?'

'No,' I said. 'But the occasion might arise.'

'Well, when it does arise, for the Lord's sake move them!'

'On my own initiative?'

'On your own flat feet for all I care,' said the Adjutant, throwing down his pen.

'Very good, sir,' I said, keeping my temper, and saluted, not noticing a tray of papers which had very foolishly been placed on top of a filing-cabinet at my right elbow. It took me some little time to collect all the papers and replace them. I am not a young man and quite unused to scrambling about under desks on all-fours. We left that kind of thing to the boys at Burgrove, I am thankful to say. But war is no respecter of persons; I quite realize that.

It was this little contretemps, I think, that made me forget, until I was outside the door, that one point still remained to be settled, and I had therefore to re-enter in order to ask where I was to put the rubber tubing.

To my mind the Adjutant's reply was absolutely inexcusable. No doubt he is a busy man; we are all busy these days. But if I am prepared to take the trouble to ask him a civil question in order to ensure that I carry out my duties correctly, the least he can do is to give a civil answer. After all, we are all in this war to help one another, are we not? Without co-operation, as I tried to tell him, the whole system falls to the ground. Besides, he was the first to complain over that business of the cinders last week. I remember his very words: 'Next time you are thinking of having a lot of smouldering ashes emptied in the ammunition store, just advise me about it beforehand, will you, Wentworth?' Very well. It was simply because of a natural anxiety to avoid any similar misunderstanding over the rubber tubing that I put my question. Surely I had a right to expect a reasonable reply?

I have half a mind to make a complaint.

THURSDAY, 27 MARCH 1941

Old Poole is back at the school, so I hear in a note from Rawlinson. Dear old chap. He left us in 1937 and has come back, I suppose, to take Collingridge's place now the latter has gone into the Navy. I don't know, I'm sure. Collingridge was our English master and Poole taught only French – and not very much of that, I'm afraid – so I don't see how it is going to work out. Probably they will share out Collingridge's work between Rawlinson and that new man Bishop. But then who is going to take IVb? It is all very muddling.

I have been driven almost to distraction by that confounded rubber tubing. I had it put in the miniature rifle range, which has been used as a dump for all kinds of unwanted bales and boxes ever since the war began; but apparently there is a plan to use the range for shooting, and somebody threw the tubing out again into the middle of the drill hall. There the Adjutant found it and made quite a scene, so I'm told; I wasn't there to defend myself, unfortunately. Why he should jump to the conclusion that *I* had put it there, goodness only knows.

The Quartermaster refuses to have it in his store, and the boiler-house seems to be locked every time I try it, so I have ordered two men to push the infernal thing under one of the huts and cover it with cinders. There seems to be no other way out. Of course I intend this to be only a temporary measure.

FRIDAY, 28 MARCH 1941
The question of the disposal of the rubber tubing is settled. Apparently the cookhouse fatigue men use it to wash down the cookhouse floor and so on, and it ought never to have been moved. No one told me this at the time, of course, or I might have been spared a great deal of worry and bother. So it is now back where it started, as I found out quite by accident this morning. I tripped over it, as a matter of fact, on my way back after inspecting the cookhouse.

Another note from Rawlinson by the afternoon post to say that Poole's trousers caught fire during the first period after 'break' yesterday. I must write for details, as I believe there is more in this than meets the eye. Poole was never quite enough of a disciplinarian, to my mind.

15 JULY 1941
A tallish sergeant came into the office this morning while I was reading a Command Order about hair-slides (A.T.S.) and said he was Scringe.

I did not follow what he meant. 'How do you mean?' I asked. 'Are you unwell?'

He said he was Sergeant Scringe.

'Do you mean your name is Scringe?' I asked him, raising

my eyebrows. It seemed to me a most extraordinary thing, though I remember a boy called Hasty, now I come to think of it, in the Upper Fourth and rather good at Greek. Not that this chap looked as if he would be much use at Greek, I must say – or Latin either for that matter. Still, there it is.

'Yes, sir, Sergeant Scringe,' he said. 'Scringe is my name and I'm a sergeant, sir – by rank of course.'

'Well, what else would you be a sergeant by?' I said – 'Royal proclamation? Or what?' I had an idea the fellow meant to be insolent, and I immediately asked him for his number and pretended to write it down in Command Orders, not having any other paper handy. I make a point of asking N.C.O.s for their numbers if they show any tendency to be truculent. It brings it home to them, I think.

Collingridge used to do the same thing at Burgrove (which still stands in its own grounds in spite of the bombs, as Gilbert said in his last letter. He always had a clever way of putting things, though the Head told me once – however, I detest gossip, and after all it's what a man *is* rather than what he *has* been that counts. Though both are important, of course.). I don't mean Collingridge used to ask the boys for their numbers, because naturally they hadn't any, except on their lockers in the boot-room and so on; it was a help with the washing and mending, Matron said. He used to ask them their ages instead: '*How* old are you, Fearnly? Ten? Dear me, I should have thought eight was nearer the mark.' He always said it worked very well, but I don't know. Boys are curious creatures.

I tried it myself once or twice, but not very successfully. Mason said, I remember, that in another eight years he would be twice as old as his father was fifty years ago, and naturally I couldn't make any comment in case it might appear to be a reflection on Mr Mason in some way. The *first* Mr Mason that would be, of course, not that the second Mr Mason's name would be Mason at all, now I come to think of it. Every master has his own way of dealing with boys, I suppose. Mine, I like to think, is to lead rather than drive.

I was thinking rather nostalgically of the old days and the smell of the hymn-books in chapel and mark-reading and so on and so forth, when the phone rang and a voice said, 'You're through.'

'Through where?' I asked.

'Hold on a moment,' the operator said. 'I'm just getting them for you.'

'Getting *who*?' I said. 'I haven't asked for anybody.'

Then a man's voice said, 'You're very faint. Can you hear me?' and somebody else asked me whether I was long distance. Of course I couldn't say without knowing where they were speaking from, and I was pointing this out when the telephone made a loud jarring noise and drowned me.

'Wentworth here,' I said.

'Hullo!' said the man's voice.

'Hullo!' I said, 'Wentworth here.'

'Hullo!' said the man.

'Hul*lo*!' I said. 'Wentworth speaking.'

'Hullo! Hullo!' said the man.

'This is Crowsfoot double-two-owe-nine-ah,' I said carefully.

'Speak up Crowsfoot,' said the operator, 'they're calling you.'

I was on the verge of losing patience when the phone on the Adjutant's desk began to ring, so I shouted, 'Hold on a moment,' and hurried across. It is always the way when the Adjutant goes out.

'Hullo!' I said, snatching up the receiver.

'Wentworth here,' said a voice.

I could hardly believe my ears.

'Hullo!' I said, 'Hullo! Hul-LO! Who is it. What is going on here?'

'Hullo!' said the man.

'Look here,' I said. 'Were you speaking to me on the other phone just now?'

'The *other* phone? What do you mean?' he said.

'I'm speaking on two phones,' I explained.

'No need to do that,' he said. 'There's a mouthpiece and receiver all in one piece on these new models. You're only giving yourself unnecessary trouble.'

'Oh, go and boil yourself!' I cried, tired of all this tom-foolery. Then I slammed the receiver down and went back to my own desk.

The telephone there was still crackling.

'Wentworth here,' I said wearily.

'Can you take a call from Bicester, sir?' asked the operator.

'I can take a call from Honolulu if there isn't a raving lunatic on the other end,' I said bitterly. However, it turned out to be the C.O. and I apologized at once, in case he had misunderstood what I had said to the operator.

'What's that, Wentworth?' he said.

'I said I was sorry I said I could take a call from Honolulu if there wasn't a raving lunatic on the other end, sir,' I said.

'What the devil d'you mean, Wentworth?' he said.

I saw I had made a mistake in bringing the wretched business up at all. But there was nothing for it but to go on with it, now it had started. 'I was speaking on two phones, sir,' I explained, 'and I couldn't make head or tail of either of them. There seemed to be a complete fool on the line –'

'There often is,' said the C.O.

'So, naturally, when the operator asked me if I could take a call from Bicester I said – jokingly, sir – that I could take one from Honolulu, provided –'

'Well, don't say it again,' said the C.O., who seemed to be in one of his testy moods. 'Send a car for me at 16.30.'

As usual in this office there was no pencil or paper for me to take the message down, and I was obliged to strike a match and make a note on the blotting-paper with the burnt end. I must remember to speak to my clerk about this absurd shortage of pencils. There is no excuse for it whatever as far as I can see. We were never short of pencils at Burgrove.

As a matter of fact as soon as I had finished my note I caught sight of a pencil under the filing-cabinet, of all places, and had to go down on my hands and knees to fish it out. Imagine my annoyance when I got to my feet to see a tallish sergeant watching me from the opposite side of the desk.

'Well?' I said, flushing. 'What do *you* want?'

He said he was Scringe.

I simply couldn't follow what the fellow meant.

22 JULY 1941

Today started badly. The C.O. complained about the jam at breakfast again, and said the toast was burnt. I do my best but really I cannot be expected to make marmalade out of thin air. Nor do I see what the fact that they have kidneys twice a week at the R.A.S.C. Mess has to do with it. They must be lucky, I suppose. As I said, there is a war on and we must just do the best we can. The Colonel became so unpleasant that I decided to change the subject and began to talk to Roberts, our Adjutant here, about Part II Orders, which I am very anxious to get clear in my head.

'By the way, Roberts,' said the Colonel suddenly, 'Major Bolt was talking to me yesterday about a Sergeant he's got down there – String, Singe – some name like that. Know anything about him?'

'Never heard of him, sir.'

'Scringe,' I said. 'Sergeant Scringe, sir. He came to see me the other day.'

'When was this, Wentworth?'

'The day you were out – you were over at Bicester, I think, sir.'

'The day the car I ordered failed to turn up, you mean, eh?' said the Colonel grimly.

'My pencil had rolled under the filing-cabinet, sir,' I explained, 'and unfortunately the note I made was not very legible, with the result that instead of 16.30 hours – '

'I know, I know,' said the Colonel in his short-tempered way. 'You had been reading a book about Waterloo so you sent the car to Wellington at 18.15. Never mind that now. What did this fellow Scringe want?'

'He didn't say, sir.'

'Well, did you ask him?'

The fact is I was very busy at the time Sergeant Scringe came in. I was speaking on two telephones, which distracted my attention, and what is more I didn't care very much for the man's manner. With a little encouragement I believe he would have become insolent. So I sent him away with a flea in his ear.

The C.O. is a fine type of soldier. I would follow him anywhere, though as a matter of fact he prefers to be on his own when he is inspecting and so on. But if he has a fault it is a lack of patience with people who have had less experience of army life and ways than he has. After all, if he were to join the staff at Burgrove, I dare say he would find himself a bit out of his depth for a term or two and glad enough to take an occasional tip from an old-stager like myself. The boot would be on the other leg there, I fancy. I shall never forget Collingridge's first term, when he walked across the piece of lawn in front of the Headmaster's study. Of course nobody had told him, so he was not really to blame in any way. I only mean that that is the sort of thing that can easily happen to anyone in those particular circumstances. It isn't quite the same thing as my forgetting to ask Sergeant Scringe what he wanted, but the analogy is close enough to show what I mean.

The C.O. and Roberts were still talking about this wretched Sergeant when I left them and went across to the office. But I soon forgot him in the normal routine of the day.

French was the first to ring up.

'Look here,' he said, 'about this A/16 of yours.'

'Yes,' I said. 'Which A/16 is that?'

(An A/16 is a thing we attach or 'subjoin', as we say, to a letter, so that the other man can tear it off and send it back to show he has had the letter it was subjoined to. If he doesn't send it, then of course we know he hasn't had it and can send him another, or have a Court of Inquiry, as the case may be.)

'Dated the fifth,' French said.

'Yes, yes. But what was it attached to?'

'It wasn't attached to anything.'

'Well, subjoined then.'

'It wasn't subjoined either. It was all by itself.'

I saw at once that there had been some mistake. Naturally one doesn't send an A/16 entirely on its own, because even if it were returned it would not prove that anything had arrived

– except the A/16, of course, and even that would have come back.

'Well,' I began, 'it's a most extraordinary thing' – and then I had an idea. 'You're not talking about a *message* with a *reference number* A/16 by any chance, are you, French?' I asked.

He said he was, and that of course explained the whole thing. We might have wasted the entire morning if I hadn't happened to hit on the only possible explanation. After that it was all more or less plain sailing. French complained that our A/16 dated the fifth cancelled our A/9 dated the third and that this in turn had cancelled our A/178 dated the twenty-fifth. He said he wouldn't have minded that, only our A/178 was in fact a cancellation of our letter number four-three oblique one-three-seven oblique A of 12th May, and he wanted to know where he stood.

'It's all perfectly simple, French,' I said. 'This four-three oblique letter was cancelled on the twenty-fifth, then it was uncancelled, and now the uncancelling has been cancelled so that the letter itself is cancelled again. Is that all right?'

'But then,' he said, 'that means there's nothing left.'

'No,' I said. 'The episode is finished.'

'You mean you don't want any nominations for the West Indies after all?'

'No,' I said. 'No, I don't think so. No. Had you got somebody you wanted to nominate?'

'No,' he said. 'Only I don't see what happens to your four-three oblique two-four-nine oblique A dated 8th June in that case.'

'Does it matter?' I asked.

He said no, he supposed it didn't, and after a word or two about things in general he rang off. French is a good officer, but he tends to fuss rather a lot about non-essentials. After all, if a thing is cancelled it is cancelled and that is all there is to be said about it. Poor old Poole took to reading through his old mark-lists in his last term or two, which I always thought rather an unhealthy sign. It's the same sort of thing in a way.

All the same, it's as well to be certain, so I rang for my clerk and told him to hunt up a letter we had written about vacancies for suitable N.C.O.s in the West Indies.

'It's in the Equipment File,' he said. 'Four-three oblique – '

'In the Equipment File!' I cried. 'What in the name of goodness is it doing in the Equipment File?'

'It's Captain Stevens' system, sir.'

Captain Stevens was Adjutant here before Captain Trevelyan, who was succeeded by the present man, Roberts.

'But Captain Trevelyan abolished all that and started a system of his own,' I objected.

'Yes, sir, but when Captain Roberts came he said that of the two he preferred Captain Stevens' system. He said it only meant looking through fifty-six files instead of a hundred-and-ninety.'

Of course I couldn't permit a lance-bombardier to say anything that appeared to criticize something an officer had done, so I sent Hotfoot (another curious name) about his business and settled down to the work of entering up the secret mail.

A Colonel Ferris came to lunch. He is something to do with National Economy, though I must say he ate a good deal. Still, he wears his trousers very short, which sets a good example, I suppose.

He asked me what we did with our old pen-nibs, and I said we wrote letters with them. It seemed to satisfy him.

12 AUGUST 1942

I am to go to a new regiment tomorrow – the 600th. I should call it 'X' or 'B' Regiment normally, for security reasons, but this unit happens to be known simply as 'X' Regiment (another letter, really, of course, but the meaning is clear, I hope), so I thought it safer to reverse the procedure and call it a number. One has to be particularly careful what one says when moving.

It is unsettling somehow to make a change after all this time, but I suppose a soldier must be prepared to up sticks and be off to the end of the world if need be. It is not that I mind, only one gets used to having the hole in the carpet on the right-hand side of the fire-place in the mess and it is disconcerting for the first day or two in the new mess to find it on the left. I have

got used to the filing system here, too, in a way, and there is
the barber in Leopold Street – quite exceptionally good and
very moderate. Goodness knows what the local man at Salisbury will be like.

The C.O. has been most kind. I am not actually appointed
Adjutant of the new unit, he says, but it will be only a matter
of days, he thinks.

13 AUGUST 1942
Well, here I am, with very mixed feelings I must say, particularly as I am not where I expected to be, but somewhere quite
different. At least I don't think I am expected to be here, unless
I made a foolish mistake in the first place, which does not seem
very likely.

The trouble began at the booking-office, where I put down
my railway warrant saying 'Crowsfoot' to the clerk – forgetting
for the moment that it was Crowsfoot *from* which I was going,
not *to* which. The clerk, with a rather impudent grin, said,
'Return?' and somebody in the queue asked me if my journey
was really necessary. I made no reply, but merely stood quietly
waiting for my ticket to be made out. It was all the more
annoying to find that the ticket, when at last I got it, was made
out to the wrong destination.

'Look here,' I said. 'I want to go to Salisbury. You've given
me a ticket to Bury St Edmunds.'

'It says Bury St Edmunds here,' he said, showing me the
warrant, and to my amazement I found that it did.

'There has been some mistake,' I began.

'Your parents', not mine,' said the clerk – a remark of which
I could make neither head nor tail. Surely he did not suppose
that my warrant had been made out by my father, even had
he been still alive, which, as a matter of fact, he is not? Of
course the clerk could not know that, but still! One does not
have warrants made out by one's parents, dead *or* alive.

Unfortunately the train came in while I was wondering
what to do, leaving me no time to ring up my old headquarters
and make certain where I was supposed to go. I still think the
C.O. said Salisbury, but on the other hand there it was in black

and white on the warrant, 'Bury St Edmunds', so rather than risk turning up late at my new unit, which creates a bad impression, I decided to jump in.

I suppose the difficulty over my ticket had muddled me, for it was not until the train had pulled out that I remembered I had forgotten to make arrangements about my luggage. I suppose it will go to Salisbury as it was labelled there, unless it stays at Crowsfoot. In any case it is extremely awkward to be in this place in borrowed pyjamas, quite apart from shaving and so on. One feels such a fool.

There were two young subalterns in my carriage who were most helpful after I had explained my troubles to them. I was doubtful at first of the wisdom of telling them where I was going until one of them said he was a spy and the other offered to take off his vest and show me the marks of the parachute-harness on his back, at which we all laughed.

'What would that prove?' I asked. 'Germans use parachutes as well, you know.'

'But haven't you seen the film?' said one of them, staring.

'What film?' I asked.

'*Next of Kin.*'

'No,' I said. 'But I've heard of it, of course.'

'Good for you. Only I thought you must have seen it when you laughed.'

'Seen it when I laughed?' I said. 'Oh, I see. You mean you thought I must have laughed when I saw it. But then I haven't seen it, as I told you.'

'No, no. What I mean is I thought you wouldn't have laughed if you hadn't seen it — '

'Naturally not,' I said. 'One doesn't laugh at what one doesn't see, does one?' He seemed a particularly incoherent young man, even as young men go today, and I turned to the other officer and asked him if he could tell me whether the 600th were at Bury St Edmunds.

He said he thought not, but believed the 500th were at a place called Parkinghurst or used to be, if that was any help. In any case, he said, the train didn't go to Bury St Edmunds or anywhere near it. This final blow quite disheartened me and in the end I decided to make the best of a bad business and get out at Parkinghurst. Rather a dull sergeant at the drill hall seemed to think I had come to pay the men, but in the end I made myself understood and he agreed to take me to see the Major.

To my amazement and, I am bound to say, distress, I found myself face to face with a man who was once, for a short time, a colleague of mine at Burgrove. In the ordinary way, naturally, I am delighted to meet old members of the staff, but Major Faggott – well really, sometimes I pretty nearly lost patience with his *laissez faire* attitude and his almost *roistering* way of going on. Not a good scholar either. However, there it was.

'Well, well, well,' he said. 'Ruffle my periwig if it isn't old Wentworth, the doyen of Burgrove. Have a whisky and tell me what brings you here. I suppose you still drink as heavily as ever?'

'I am on my way to join the 600th,' I replied, ignoring his last remark, 'and I thought I would report here – '

'This is the 500th,' he said.

'I know,' I said, 'but unfortunately I got into the wrong train for Bury St Edmunds – '

'Bury St Edmunds!' said Major Faggott (he never scrupled to interrupt in the old days, I remember). 'But the 600th aren't at Bury St Edmunds. All this is very peculiar, Wentworth. I am inclined to think you are a deserter.'

The fool then warned me that anything I said would be taken down in triplicate and used in evidence against me, and asked me what I had done with my luggage.

'I have sent it to Salisbury,' I said shortly.

'An excellent plan. Then when you get posted to a unit in Newcastle and take the wrong train for Haverfordwest you'll find your luggage waiting for you. The only thing is, what are you going to do in the meantime?'

'If you will direct me to a hotel,' I began, rather stiffly – but Major Faggott would not hear of it, and very generously offered me a bed and the loan of a pair of pyjamas. They are rather more gaudy than my usual choice, as one would expect,

but it would have been churlish to refuse. I am sure he means
well, but, well, I suppose we have rather different ideas of what
is and what is *not* done.

14 AUGUST 1942

We must wait and see what the morrow will bring forth. Major
Faggott says I am to regard myself as attached here pending
posting. 'We can always do with another officer,' he said at
breakfast; 'it makes the messing easier.'

'But look here, sir,' I expostulated. 'I've been posted to the
600th. I really think I ought to be getting along.'

'I'll fix that,' he said. 'I'll speak to Charlie about you,' and
explained in answer to my inquiry that Charlie was A.G.6. I
did not quite like to say that I was unaware who or what
A.G.6 might be, and was therefore obliged to let the matter
drop. I suppose it is all right, but really it all seems a little
irregular.

'What are we going to do with him?' asked the Major
suddenly. 'We can't very well make him O.C. Transport,
because there isn't any. At least, we could, of course, in case
some comes along.'

'Gas Officer,' said a tall thin man who had just come in.
'Where's the *Mirror*?'

'By the way, this is Hobson – Wentworth. Hobson is my
gunnery expert. You wouldn't think he had a glass eye, would
you?'

'How do you do?' I said. 'I certainly shouldn't. In fact I
can hardly tell the difference even now.'

'Very tactful,' said Faggott, slapping his leg and laughing
like a madman. 'You've made a friend for life there, Wentworth. He says he can hardly tell the difference, Hobson, old
boy. The same glassy look in each of them, eh? What?'

'I'm afraid I fail to see the joke, sir,' I said coldly. The fact
is, the Major's laughter seemed to me to be in the worst possible
taste. After all, one doesn't laugh at another man's infirmities.

'The joke is he hasn't got a glass eye,' said Faggott, rolling
about in his chair in the most unseemly way. 'Which did you
think it was? The dull-green one, or the one with all those red

streaks in it? Oh, dear, oh, dear, Wentworth, you'll be the
death of me yet. "Hardly tell the difference", wasn't it? I must
make a note of that.'

'I'm afraid I know very little about gas, Hobson,' I said, to
change the conversation. 'I mean, I should have to have a
course of instruction before I could conscientiously take on the
appointment.'

However, Hobson assured me that that wouldn't be necessary. 'This is a new unit, you see,' he explained. 'Just forming.
So nobody knows anything about anything. You'll just have
to pick it up as you go along.'

'Like a crossing-sweeper,' added Major Faggott, with his
usual lack of taste.

Apparently my first duty as Gas Officer is to go up in an
aeroplane. I was rather surprised at this, naturally, for I failed
to see the connexion, but Major Faggott explained that we had
been ordered to send an observer on an air co-operation exercise and I was the obvious person to go. He said he believed, as
a matter of fact, that the message was intended for another
unit, but it had come to us so we must just carry out instructions.

'But I have never flown,' I objected.

'It's quite easy,' said Hobson. 'You just get in and sit still and
then you get out again when you get back to the ground – '

'Or sooner, as the case may be,' said Faggott.

'You won't be expected to take the controls,' added Hobson.
'The R.A.F. have undertaken to provide a qualified driver.'

'Pilot,' I corrected, *sotto voce*.

15 AUGUST 1942

It has been a most interesting experience. The exercise was at
night, which I hadn't expected, so that one was unable to see
the ground; but, of course, it was the same for the pilot and
the rest of the crew, so I must not grumble.

The R.A.F. were most kind. They gave me a parachute
before we started and explained how I was to use it. 'You
probably won't have to,' my pilot told me, 'unless there are
hostiles about and we get pranged.'

'Pranged?' I said.

'Yes.'

'I see,' I said, though I confess I did not quite follow what he meant.

'In that case, just nip out, count three slowly and pull this thing.'

'Right,' I said briskly. 'Does one come down with much of a bump?'

'Oh, no,' he said. 'Unless the parachute fails to open.'

'I see,' I said.

It is not very easy to get into a bomber at night, and unfortunately, when I had got in, there was no seat for me and I had to squat on my parachute.

'By the way,' said the pilot, when we were all inside, 'you've come as an observer, haven't you?'

'Yes,' I said. 'Yes, yes.'

'What are you going to observe, particularly?'

'Well,' I said, 'nothing particularly. Just general observation.' The fact is nobody had remembered to tell me what I was supposed to be doing.

'Afraid you won't see much tonight,' he said. 'Except the stars.'

'It doesn't matter, thanks,' I said. 'I'm a Gas Officer, really. At least, I hope to be when I have had a little more experience.'

'I see,' said the pilot.

Soon after that he started up the engines and conversation ceased. It is rather noisy in a bomber when the engines are going – 'revving', as they say – and one has to shout to make oneself heard.

'How high are we now?' I shouted, when we had been roaring along for about five minutes. It is quite impossible to get any idea of height when you are flying in the dark.

'We haven't started yet,' shouted the pilot. 'I'm just warming her up.'

'Oh,' I said, feeling rather a fool. I suppose in the noise and darkness I had got rather confused.

However, it was much the same when we did start, except that one had to shout rather louder. The machine was very steady, and after a time I became more used to the noise and began to get ready to observe. Then, without any warning, there was a sudden bump and the aeroplane dropped like a lift.

I kept my head, and turned inquiringly to the pilot. 'Pranged?' I shouted. But he shook his head and said, 'Cloud.'

'I see,' I cried, but I don't think he heard me.

Nothing happened for another ten minutes and I began to grow aware that my seat was far from comfortable. By pure ill-chance, in endeavouring to adjust the parachute on which I was sitting, I caught hold of the wrong handle and something came right away in my hand. I rose to a crouching position and, turning round to see what was amiss, was horrified to see a volume of white material, like dough, pouring out of the wrapping. I did not know what to do and the pilot, not realizing my predicament, added to my difficulties by turning the machine abruptly on its side so that I was thrown off my balance and forced to put out a hand to save myself. Instantly there was a sharp report and some kind of flare or firework was projected from the underside of the aeroplane.

The pilot said something which I did not catch, for I had my hands too full at the moment to attend to him. It is a skilled task, I am informed, to repack a parachute in the most favourable conditions, and I do not believe it can be done in a crouching position in an aeroplane in the dark. There is a great deal of material to cope with, for one thing.

My great fear was that the thing would master me and spread all over the aircraft so that we should all be choked or, if not that, that the pilot would no longer be able to see the controls. It seemed to spring up after me the moment I rose from a sitting position, and do what I would, folds and loops of the stuff kept oozing out from under me at the sides and back.

'Sit tight,' I said to myself, 'and keep your nerve', and I remember thinking what a story this would make to tell to the boys, if ever I should get back to the old life at Burgrove. I think this helped to steady me.

Suddenly I felt a tap on my shoulder and carefully turning about I found that the navigator was trying to communicate with me.

'What do you say?' I cried. 'I can't hear you.'

'Your shirt's hanging out at the back,' he roared.

I realized then that the parachute had got hitched to my Sam Browne, which I had put on for the flight, and it was this, of course, that had given it a tendency to rise up in the air when I moved. I unhitched it and had practically no further trouble, I am thankful to say.

'I am afraid you were too busy to observe much,' said the pilot when we landed.

'Not at all,' I said. 'It has been a most interesting experience for me.'

'It has for all of us,' he said, which I thought very nice of him. After all, one flight more or less in a bomber, even at night, is all in the day's work for its gallant crew.

[*There is, of course, a vast mass of material in the war-time diaries from which I might quote. But this is perhaps enough to show that my friend Wentworth carried with him into the army those same qualities of solid worth and sound logical common sense that served him so well in his peacetime profession. Mr Wentworth returned to Burgrove after his demobilization in January 1946, and the Memorandum with which this book ends shows that he has lost little or nothing of his old flair for the big occasion.*]

# Memorandum from
# A. J. Wentworth, B.A.

**TO THE HEADMASTER**                              6 MARCH 1946

Sir – It is with considerable regret that I inform you that things
cannot go on as they are at present unless some change is made.
Had it been some small matter such as the school radiators,
which have been stone cold for the last three days, I should
have come to see you in the ordinary way, or the shortage of
nibs and blotting-paper about which I have spoken fifty times
to Rawlinson already, but it is *not*. A schoolmaster has plenty
to do without that sort of thing in any case. But either there is
discipline in a school or there is not. That is my point. And if
there is no discipline I for one will have no part in it. I have
not given up what might have been the best years of my life to
Burgrove, in order to have my boot-laces tied to the legs of my
desk at the end of it and so be prevented from rising to my feet
when parents are shown into my classroom, as I always do.
This is not the first time an attempt has been made to make me
look ridiculous in front of other people, nor is it the last, as I
am well aware, after seeing Matron sneaking into your study
this very afternoon with some garbled version no doubt of an
incident outside the School Museum which could never have
happened if people would stop misrepresenting my slightest
action and making mare's nests at my expense out of nothing
at all.

I have always done my best and put the interests of the
school first, but if it is to be put about that I made an unpro-
voked attack with a cutlass on a boy of eleven years during the
after-lunch rest-period, I can only say that the sooner I tender
my resignation the better for all concerned. That the boy,

Malcolm, was not even a member of my Mathematical Set would have been enough, one might have supposed, to scotch such a ridiculous story at the outset. But apparently it is not. The sword was not, as it happens, a cutlass, but a scimitar. There is no cutlass in the School Museum. But those who are responsible for spreading unfounded gossip of this kind about me are not likely to allow a trifle of that nature to stand in their way. I should be thankful, perhaps, that I am not accused of throwing assegais, of which a large number were presented to the school last term by Mr Tallboys and hang on the west wall at present, pending some other arrangement. He has also promised an elk's head and some West African wood-carvings.

I am determined to put a stop to this kind of thing. I have as much right to handle the weapons in the Museum as anyone. More. The Museum is in my charge, as was settled at the Masters' Meeting in January, and Malcolm had no business to be there in the rest-period. Does Matron deny my right to take down the scimitar and dust it? If so, let her deny it to my face and I will very soon make clear to her where her jurisdiction ends and mine begins. She would be better employed in seeing that the boys are resting on their beds after lunch than in trying to interfere with the way I run the Museum.

I have little more to say. I consider that Malcolm's behaviour in dashing out of the Museum crying, 'Spare me! Spare me!' the moment he caught sight of me with the sword in my hand was little short of downright impertinence. The boy should be thrashed. That I should run after him to tell him to be quiet was not only a perfectly natural thing to do, it was my duty. And I shall continue to do my duty, with or without Matron's permission, for so long as I remain on the Staff here at Burgrove.

That that time is likely to be short we are both well aware. My resignation is in your hands. Should you wish to accept it, there is no more to be said, except to thank you for many happy years and much kindness and to ask you as a special favour that some arrangement be made to expedite the return of my laundry before I depart. I should of course in the ordinary way approach Matron on this matter, but you will understand, in the circumstances, that that is quite impossible. I have a few books which may be of use to the boys' library.

Should you desire me to withdraw my resignation I will do so, provided:

That a full apology is made by Matron in the presence of the whole Staff.

That Malcolm is thrashed, or otherwise punished at your discretion.

That other arrangements are made for the management of the School Museum, which it is now painful for me to enter.

I will take steps to deal with the comparatively trivial matter of the boot-laces myself.

*(Signed)* ARTHUR J. WENTWORTH

[*A copy of the note sent by the Headmaster to Wentworth, in answer to the foregoing Memorandum, has come into my hands. It seems to clear the matter up.*]

FROM THE HEADMASTER

Dear A.J. – I don't know what all the fuss is about. Matron came to see me this afternoon about gym-shoes, not cutlasses.

I have seen Malcolm and told him not to be a silly little fool.

The man I had with me when I entered your classroom this morning was not a parent, or not, at any rate, in the sense in which we use the term; he had come to see about the break-down in the central heating system. I cannot allow you to resign on the grounds that you were unable to stand up when a plumber came into your room.

So please put your personal feelings on one side – and remember, Wentworth, that the School must come first.

*(Signed)* G.S.

P.S. I have just completed arrangements for an old friend of yours, Major Faggott, to join us next term in Rawlinson's place. He will probably be willing to take over the Museum, if you really wish to give it up.

By all means use your own initiative about the boot-laces.

The Papers of
A. J. Wentworth, B.A. (Ret'd)

# At Fenport

A young fellow called at my cottage this morning to ask whether I would care to become a Vice-President of the Fenport Football Club. Monday is the day on which Mrs Bretton takes my laundry home with her and, of course, I was expecting nothing of the kind.

'Come in, come in,' I said. 'There's nothing else that I know of, Mrs Bretton, thank you. I put it all together in the bathroom.'

My visitor said he was Ernie Craddock from the garage and happened to be passing. I am old enough to remember the days when he would just have stood there, twisting his cap about awkwardly in his hands – not Craddock of course, but a much older man of the same age – and saying nothing. But times have changed. 'Wash day, eh?' he said. 'Shan't keep you a tick, though. The thing being, what about you as a Vice-Pre of the club?'

I said, when I understood what it was that he was trying to say, that it was a great honour to be asked and one that I greatly appreciated. 'What would my duties be exactly?' I asked, and he told me that I should not have to do anything actually. 'It's just the subscription, see,' he explained.

'I see,' I said. 'Well, I shall have to think it over – Yes, Mrs Bretton? What is it now?'

She is an excellent creature in many ways, and cooks my lunch and so on except on Sundays, when her husband is at home, but she does not understand that there are times when ones does *not* wish to be bothered with household matters.

'No, not those,' I said, to be rid of her. 'The thin blue stripe this week, please. I was never a great footballer, I fear, Mr Craddock,' I went on, 'so that if there were any question of taking an active – '

'No refereeing, eh? Is that it?' he cried, breaking out into loud laughter, in which I confess I did not join. I suppose he intended a reference to a trivial incident that occurred towards the end of the cricket season, when I was unexpectedly asked to umpire a local match. The whole thing has been ridiculously exaggerated. It is nonsense to say that I deliberately tripped up one of the Fenport batsmen in the middle of the pitch and then gave him out. I have umpired hundreds of games at Burgrove Preparatory School in my time, including one or two First Eleven fixtures when Rawlinson was away, and such a thing has never happened before. I had a perfect right to cross over from one side of the pitch to the other, as soon as I noticed that a left-hander had arrived at my end – indeed it was my duty so to do.

'The bowler was entirely to blame, Mr Craddock,' I said with some warmth, when he had had his laugh out. 'He had no business to deliver the ball without first ascertaining that I, as umpire, was in a position to adjudicate if called upon to do so – as in fact I was.'

'The bowler, eh?' he repeated, breaking out afresh. People often laugh a great deal, I have noticed, when they realize they are getting the worst of an argument.

'Certainly,' I said. I had no doubt in my own mind that the bowler was to blame. The result of his precipitancy was that in crossing the pitch I inadvertently collided with the batsman, who was running a leg-bye, and to add to the confusion he, in falling, made an involuntary sweeping movement with his bat and brought down the batsman from the other end. Meanwhile the stumps had been thrown down and, on appeal from the wicket-keeper, I had no option but to give the decision 'run out'. Even, as I explained later to the Fenport captain, had I been in any way to blame, there is no provision in the Laws for 'Obstruction of the striker', whether by an umpire or anyone else. It was simply one of those instances of bad luck, which sometimes occur in cricket and must be accepted in a sporting spirit.

'I thought I should have died,' Craddock said, beating his hands against his knees in a rather affected way. 'The three of you lying there, and you on your back with your finger up calling "Out!". "OUT!" says you. "Out! Who's out?" says somebody. "Both of 'em?" And then, on top o' the lot – '

I enjoy a good joke as well as any man, but I fail to see the humour in what was, after all, a straightforward cricketing dilemma. It is true that, on being asked amid some laughter which of the two batsmen I had given out, I declined to give a ruling; but my difficulty was that both of them – indeed, all three of us – lay at a point roughly equidistant from the two wickets, and I was unable without reference to *Wisden* to say how the Law stood. I therefore, rightly I think, referred the matter to my colleague at the bowler's end, who called very belatedly, 'No ball!' and ordered the game to proceed – a highly improper decision, in my opinion. Be that as it may, no one had a right to criticize my own handling of the incident who has not himself been faced with a similar situation on the cricket field – at short notice too, remember.

I was endeavouring to point this out to Craddock, and growing a little heated at his continued silly laughter when Mrs Bretton, perhaps fortunately, came down again to say that she had found my spectacles in 'the upstairs place' as she prefers to call it.

'I have my reading glasses here, thank you, Mrs Bretton,' I said, taking them out of my pocket.

'These'll be the others then – for looking out the window and that,' she replied. 'Though what you'd be wanting with them in the upstairs – '

'Never mind that now,' I said sharply. 'Just leave them on the table, please.' I have no wish to hurt her feelings, but I really do not feel that I can enter into long discussions about where and why I have left this, that or the other thing. I had enough of that at Burgrove, towards the end.

Craddock took himself off soon afterwards, remarking that a guinea was the usual thing and adding that he had had 'a wonderful time' – a glib phrase, meaningless in the circumstances, which I suppose he has picked up from his betters or the wireless or somewhere. I saw him to the gate and was just too late to shout at Sidney Megrim's infernal terrier. He pays no attention whatever to the by-laws relating to footpaths, and I shall really have to speak to him about it. To Megrim, that is to say. It is useless to speak to the dog.

When I had dealt with that, it was time to go down to the village for tobacco, and with one thing and another my *Telegraph* crossword had to be left till after lunch. Not that it matters, in a way. I am no stickler for a rigid routine, I am thankful to say. It is just that one likes to have the afternoon free for other things.

A letter from Gilbert, who will be following me into retirement in another five years or so, I suppose, set me thinking about the old days after tea. Or rather, set me thinking after tea about the old days. One likes to be accurate – I have my mathematical training to thank for that – without being too fussy, and as a matter of fact it was after breakfast I happened to be thinking about. This being Monday the Stationery Cupboard should have been open between 9 and 9.30 a.m., and I could not help worrying. Gilbert has had a lot of experience, of course; he knows about the pink blotting-paper for Common Room use only, naturally. But experience isn't everything, now that he has taken over full responsibility. One has to be pretty firm at times, with a lot of boys clamouring round for pens and rubbers and so on, to which very often they have no right. For want of a nail, they say, the battle was lost, and the same thing applies, up to a point, to nibs and Common Entrance. Of course, it is none of my business now, and nobody I dare say is indispensable, difficult though it may be at first for my colleagues to realize it. 'We struggle along as best we can,' Gilbert very kindly writes, 'without you.'

It is a relief, in a way, to be free of the worries and anxieties of a senior master at a preparatory school, but life without responsibility and duties, as I told them all at the Presentation, is an empty thing. ('As empty as a swimming bath without any water in it,' I could not resist adding, a reference which they greatly appreciated to the time when, through an absurd misunderstanding, I opened the wastepipe on the morning of the School Diving Competition. A joke against oneself helps to relieve the tension, I have often found, even on a serious occasion; though my heart was heavy enough, naturally, as I stood there with my right hand resting on the mahogany bureau subscribed for by many old Burgrovians, as well as past and present colleagues.) 'I hope,' I said to them, when the laughter had died down, 'that I shall find no less useful work to do at my new home in Hampshire.' This, for some reason, started the younger boys laughing again – through over-excitement, I think.

I certainly intend to take as full a part in the life of the village as my reading and other tasks and interests allow. But these things take time. One cannot become a churchwarden overnight. I should have thought that any fool would understand that. I thought so at least until this evening, when I sauntered down to the post office to get my reply off to Gilbert.

I was standing quietly at the stamp counter, waiting until the sub-postmistress had finished selling a pair of canvas shoes, when quite by chance I happened to overhear a conversation between two men at the far end of the shop, one of whom I recognized by his voice to be Mellish from the chemist's.

'Who's that little old chap went up street just now, then?' the other man asked.

'Struts along?' Mellish asked. 'Shortish, and looks over the top of his specs? Name of Wentworth. Elm Cottage. Didn't you hear?'

The other man said no, and Mellish then gave a very inaccurate and one-sided account of the umpiring incident to which I have already briefly referred. I had half a mind to go across at once and point out the fact (which Mellish had deliberately omitted) that it was the bowler who had been to blame. It would have served Mellish right to be made to look foolish in public. But, to tell the truth, I am sick and tired of the silly business, and besides that I strongly object to eavesdropping in any shape or form. I should have made my way out of the shop, had there been any way of doing so un-observed. As it was, I was forced to remain and listen to the rest of the conversation, distasteful though it was.

'What is 'e, then, when he's not playing the giddy-goat?' the second man asked. (Giddy-goat, indeed! My old friends at Burgrove would have something to say about *that*.) 'What's 'e do?'

'Do?' Mellish said. 'Nothing.'

'How's he manage that, then?'

'Easy,' Mellish said. 'Starts right in at it after breakfast, so I'm told, and keeps on without a break till bedtime. A proper gentleman, old Mother Bretton calls him.'

'I should like a threepenny stamp at once, please, Mrs Enticott,' I said loudly. 'I am in rather a hurry, as I have a great deal to do.'

I propose to leave the matter there. At my age one has learnt to treat idle, ill-informed gossip with the contempt it deserves. All the same, I shall be surprised if Mellish does not take a very different view of my character before the year is out.

# A Misunderstanding at the Greengrocer's

I am not at all sure that time is really saved by this modern habit of abbreviation. The longest way round is often the shortest way home, as my old nurse never tired of telling me. She is dead now, of course, but the principle of the thing remains. 'Just you put one leg in at a time, Master Arthur,' she used to say. 'Then we shan't have you toppling over backwards into all that Plasticine.' She had a fund of wisdom, rest her soul, and the world would be a better place if there were more of her like about today.

Her words came back to me at the greengrocer's this morning. I mean about the shortest way home, naturally – not the other. At my age one doesn't topple over backwards at the greengrocer's or anywhere else; or at least, if one does (and the truth is, whatever Miss Edge might say, that the place was abominably crowded and I for one would rather step a little too close to the carrot rack than inconvenience a lady any day), the reasons are different. What made me think of my old nurse was this silly trick of saying 'three' instead of 'three pence' or 'three-pennyworth'. Surely we are not all in such a rush to get wherever we are going that we have time only for monosyllables? The result in any case is to waste time as often as not, as happened this morning when I said I wanted some brussels sprouts and asked the price.

'Ten,' the man said.

I naturally supposed he was inquiring how many I wanted and told him it was just for myself, to go with a chop, and thought perhaps eight would do, if they were large ones. When

I am more used to shopping for myself I shall know in a flash, but at present I am rather feeling my way.

He is one of those sandy-haired young men, always trying to do six things at once. 'Not up there, Fred,' he shouted. 'They're under the caulies. What did you want, then?'

'About eight, I think,' I began, but broke off because he was telling a lady that the lettuces she was fingering were fresh in today. Then he took fourpence from a thrustful woman who came up with a lemon, and began to shovel up vast quantities of sprouts in a scoop.

'Got a sack?' he asked me.

'Good heavens!' I said. 'Are those for me? All I wanted – '

'Make up your mind,' he said. 'Eight pound, you *said*. If it's for Mrs Odding,' he added, speaking over his shoulder to a girl in a white overall, 'she has the Cos.'

I began to lose patience with these constant unmannerly interpolations. 'I do not care tuppence, young man,' I said warmly, 'whether Mrs Odding has the Cos – or the flu either, for that matter. All I want is a little civility, and some sprouts.'

One of those odd silences fell over the shop while I was speaking, and it may be that a sudden consciousness that heads were turning in my direction put me momentarily off my guard. At any rate, in making way for a woman who came bustling past me with a push-chair, I took an incautious pace backwards and fouled the carrot rack. It is absurd to have such an insecure structure in a busy shop. After all, one can move about perfectly freely in a fishmonger's without bringing a hundredweight of haddock about one's ears; or in a hat shop or chemist's for that matter, *mutatis mutandis*, now that they no longer pile up sponges and loofahs in inadequate wire baskets. There ought to be more consideration and common sense. Ironmongers hang their surplus shovels and brooms and so on from the ceiling, and though that might not do in every case it shows what can be achieved by the exercise of a little imagination. At Burgrove Preparatory School the boys' bowler hats (for travelling, etc.) used to be kept piled up on a shelf at elbow level, but soon after my arrival there as Assistant Mathematical Master they were moved to a high cupboard out of reach – another case in point.

Everybody was very kind and helpful, but in the end I left without buying any sprouts and went, almost directly, to Gooch's for tobacco. He also sells walking-sticks, though I don't quite see the connexion. Something to do with the open air perhaps, unless briar was once used for both – I mean for pipes as well as for walking-sticks, or rather the other way round. But that hardly seems likely.

Miss Edge was in Gooch's and shook her finger at me in a way I do not much admire.

'What's this I hear about you pelting Mrs Odding with carrots, Mr Wentworth?' she said immediately.

The speed with which gossip, and highly inaccurate gossip at that, flies about a small place like Fenport still astonishes me, though I have been there six months or more now and ought to be finding my feet. It was bad enough in a Common Room, but here!

'Pelting Mrs Odding!' I cried, hardly able to believe my ears. 'Why, I – '

'With carrots,' she repeated, nodding. 'Over at Wrightson's. *And* calling her names, by all accounts. I didn't even know you knew her.'

'I do *not*,' I replied, colouring up. 'What is more, Miss Edge, sorry as I am to scotch so succulent a snake at birth, she was not even in the shop at the time. I merely – '

'Oh, Mr Wentworth!' she said. 'Behind her back! That *was* naughty.'

'One does not pelt people with carrots behind their backs,' I began heatedly; but noticing that Mrs French and her little boy had entered the shop and seemed to be listening I broke off and asked for an ounce of Richmond Curly Cut.

'Five,' the girl said.

'No, one,' I corrected her.

'Five shillings,' said Old Gooch, intervening. 'Just gone up.'

Five shillings! And I can remember when it was seven-pence. Still, there it is. One must move with the times or go under, as happened to a poor old friend of mine when haircuts went up to one-and-six. After all, it is cheaper to have one's teeth out now than it was in the old days, so that one thing balances another up to a point.

Miss Edge was nowhere to be seen when I turned to continue our conversation, and I made my way home in a thoughtful frame of mind. It is idle to concern oneself over-much with the small contretemps of every day; gossip-mongers will make mountains out of molehills, do what one will. None the less it distressed me to think that this Mrs Odding might be led to believe that I had spoken rudely about her, if (as was more than probable) some garbled version of the incident were to reach her ears. It would be better, I decided – rightly I still think – to ring the lady up and explain the whole thing quite simply, before Miss Edge or anybody else had a chance to upset her with ill-natured tittle-tattle. But of course that meant that I must waste no time at all.

There is only one Odding in the book – it is an unusual name, I think – so there was no difficulty about that.

'Odding here,' said a man's voice, when I got through.

'I have just come from the greengrocer's,' I explained, ' – that is, I wonder, could I speak to Mrs Odding, please?'

'For you,' I heard him say. 'Chap from the greengrocer's. Got a mouthful of potatoes to get rid of, by the sound of it.'

If a lifetime's schoolmastering has taught me nothing else (as it certainly has), I have at last learned to disregard trivial rudenesses. Of course, in this instance, I was no doubt not intended to overhear what was said, but I could not help wondering whether Mr Odding has ever paused to consider what his *own* voice may sound like when distorted by the telephone.

'Yais? What then? Mrs Odding spiks,' another voice said.

'Oh, Mrs Odding,' I said – with rather a sinking heart, to tell the truth – 'I am sorry to trouble you, but I just wanted to clear up a small matter, a silly little incident at the green – '

'Is arrived,' Mrs Odding said. 'He is come O.K. Beets and all.'

'Yes, yes,' I said. 'This is another matter. I happened to be in Wrightson's this afternoon when one of the assistants – '

'Is right?'

'Wrightson's, Mrs Odding. With a W, you know. One of the assistants, the sandy-haired one actually, mentioned that you preferred the Cos, the lettuce, you understand – '

'Alwais,' she said firmly. 'Never the other. It is becoss of the wind.'

'I see. Well – '

'Up she comes, else. With Cos, no. If he is not Cos, back she goes. You know me?'

'No, Mrs Odding,' I said. 'That is what I wanted to explain.' I did not, as a matter of fact, want to do anything of the kind. I am not in any sense a Little Englander: some of my best friend are Balts and Slovenes and so on; and I am well aware of the importance of reaching a close understanding with people who have not had the same advantages as we have – or perhaps one ought to say not the same kind of advantages, to avoid the risk of misunderstanding. But, really! When it comes to clearing up a silly little affair in a greengrocer's one would rather have to do with one's own kidney.

'Mrs Odding,' I went on, speaking slowly and distinctly, 'I simply rang up to ask you to take no notice of any stupid stories you may hear about a trifling incident in the greengrocer's this afternoon. When I tell you that people are already going about saying that I pelted you with carrots, Mrs Odding, at a time when, as you and I know perfectly well – '

'Here, I've had enough of this,' said Mr Odding's voice. 'Who the devil are you? And what do you mean by trying to frighten my wife with a lot of damn balderdash about carrots? Ringing up in the middle of tea and scaring a woman out of her wits after all she's been through these last months – '

I allow no one to take that tone with me, least of all when I am attempting to make an apology.

'My name is Wentworth,' I said coldly, 'and I would have you know that – '

'Aha!' he said. 'So *that's* it.' And rang off.

Two minutes later the phone rang again, and I supposed it would be this man, Odding, come to his senses and anxious to explain himself. But it turned out to be Harcutt, a solicitor whom I have met once or twice at the library and so on.

'I say, Wentworth,' he said, 'speaking as a friend, is it true you called Miss Edge a succulent snake at the chemist's this afternoon?'

One really has no patience with this kind of folly.

'If you are thinking of joining the Old Women's Scandal-mongering Society, Harcutt,' I suggested, 'you had better try to get *some* of your facts right. In the first place, Miss Edge and I met not at the chemist's but at Gooch's.'

'That certainly alters the situation,' he said.

'And secondly, I called her no such thing. I should have thought you knew me well enough by this time. The amount of petty gossip and trouble-making that goes on in this place – '

'Well, keep your hair on, Wentworth,' he said – an expression I have always disliked. 'I was only joking.'

'And while we are about it,' I told him, 'here is a further bit of information for you. I did not throw carrots at Mrs Odding in the greengrocer's either.'

'You didn't?'

'No.'

'Then why mention it?'

'Because I have no doubt that it is all over the village by now.'

'Wait a minute, Wentworth,' he said. 'Are you suggesting that things have reached such a pitch that the fact that you *didn't* throw carrots at somebody is red-hot news?'

'Oh, go and boil yourself, Harcutt,' I said. He is a good chap in many ways, but I was not in the mood for that kind of schoolboy facetiousness. All this fuss over buying a few sprouts, and even then I did not get any.

I took up the dictionary after supper, to calm my mind, and looked up 'briar'. Apparently they don't make pipes from the prickly kind, but from the root of a sort of heath, which makes the connexion between tobacco and walking-sticks all the more mysterious. The word comes from the French *bruyère*, to my surprise. I had always thought it a kind of cheese.

# Brains Trust

The Conservative Association holds from time to time what they call a Brains Trust. St Mark's Hall is not a very cheerful place for it, in many ways; the walls are dark green and tend to sweat, and of course rows and rows of rush-bottomed chairs never suggest cosiness. Still, people come. I dare say they like to see our local M.P., Sir Arnold Bantry, who is always on the 'panel', and other notabilities from Fenport and West Acre and even farther afield. It makes an evening, as Mrs Wheeler puts it.

I little thought, when I first strolled along to St Mark's six months or so ago, that I should one day be 'on the panel' myself. But Mrs Dalrymple has been most pressing. 'Everybody's tired of these endless barristers and journalists,' she told me. 'We need fresh blood, a new outlook. Do say yes.' At first I demurred. One does not like to stand in the way of the younger people. Besides, my knowledge of the world is to some extent departmentalized and, though I make it my business to take a lively interest in everything that goes on around me, I might well be floored by a question on, let us say, the Middle East oil situation – or as I told Mrs Dalrymple – anything about marital relationships, which I have never had. However, she entirely misunderstood my point.

'There's nothing to be frightened of, Mr Wentworth,' she said. 'The audience are very friendly and the Chairman will help you all he can – Sidney Megrim is *so* good – and see you safely through those "beginner's nerves".'

The idea that I, after a lifetime's schoolmastering, might be alarmed at the thought of facing a roomful of middle-aged ladies in a tuppeny-ha'penny place like Fenport was really too much. I made a somewhat emphatic reply, which Mrs Dalrymple took as an acceptance, so that I found myself committed before I had really considered the matter fully. 'Next Thursday, then, at 8 p.m.,' she said gaily. 'And the very best of luck.'

The short notice made me wonder whether somebody else had fallen out at the last moment, and the suspicion became a virtual certainty when the Chairman introduced the members of the panel to the audience, getting my name right but adding that I was an authority on Elizabethan Drama and had been in my day a well-known amateur actor. No doubt somebody had forgotten to alter the notes given to him about the original panellist. It is all in the day's work, but even so! 'In my day', if you please. One is not a hundred and fifty. I have never acted, as it happens, but if I had I dare say I could act as well today as ever I did. Better, very likely, with all the added experience of life and character and so on that the years bring. Everybody clapped politely, as they do at these affairs, and the Chairman read out the first question before I had a chance to put the matter right.

It was about woman's proper place being in the home and Sir Arnold, who spoke first, made the apt point that it was the Conservative policy to encourage women to devote to their homes the time and energy demanded by their proud positions as wives and mothers, while at the same time developing in the larger world outside those public and civic qualities upon which so much depended. He then criticized the Socialists for their attitude to the Early Closing Act of (if I remember rightly) 1922, and was reminded of an amusing incident in which he missed an important appointment in London through some misunderstanding about spaghetti. I forget how he linked it up, but it was all very skilfully done and showed how a practised speaker can turn the most unlikely subject into grist for his mill.

A Mr Philip Tallboys said he agreed with every word the Member had said, and had little to add except it was no good saying that woman's proper place was in the home unless you first made sure that she *had* a home to take her proper place in. The Conservatives had no reason to be ashamed of their record in providing homes for the people. He is a chartered accountant, with a habit of slouching down in his chair and tapping his finger-tips together that struck me as a shade patronizing at a public meeting of this kind. Miss Gorman, on the other hand, who followed him with an interesting account of her life in a biological laboratory, leaned right forwards with her hands clasping her bag and described the 'worthwhileness' (to use her own phrase) of dissecting water-beetles and so on with an eagerness to which the front row of Fenport housewives were slow to respond. Or so I thought. It is a capital mistake to try to win sympathy by over-emphasis. Let the facts speak for themselves – such at least was my method when teaching geometry at Burgrove – instead of repeatedly urging their importance and interest.

While Miss Gorman was speaking I caught the eye of a man about four rows back who was putting a sweet of some kind in his mouth. Old habits die hard and I gave him a sharp look. I suppose there is no definite rule about eating at public meetings, but it would look very odd if those on the platform started putting toffees in their mouths, and what is sauce for the goose ought surely, as a matter of ordinary politeness, to be sauce for the gander. At any rate the man I caught at it clearly felt uneasy, for he gave a little cough and put his hand up to his mouth again – an old trick, designed to make one think that that was what he was doing the first time. Thereafter, whenever I glanced in his direction he instantly stopped chewing and stared straight ahead with rigid jaws. It was annoying to be unable to tell the silly fellow that a man with my training could see through a dozen better dodges than that. I remember a boy called Mason who took the rubber out of the metal holder on the end of his pencil and substituted pieces of mint humbug, cut to fit. He is an aeroplane designer now, they tell me, and putting his ingenuity, one hopes, to more worthwhile ends. But he very nearly fooled me at the time.

I mention this small incident only to explain why my attention was momentarily distracted when the Chairman called my name.

'Eh? What's that?' I asked.

'We are hoping,' he said amid some laughter, 'that you would have something to say on this question.'

'What question is that?'

'We have been discussing,' the Chairman said, with a long-suffering air that rather nettled me, 'whether woman's proper place is in the home.'

'Have you, indeed,' I replied. 'I was under the impression that you had been discussing whether the proper place for water-beetles was the Conservative Party.' This sally, which was of course intended, in part at least, to be in jocular vein, was very well received by the audience. Sir Arnold, however, saw fit to take offence.

'We certainly get all sorts at our meetings,' he remarked.

'It is quite clear, at any rate,' put in Miss Gorman, 'that the proper place for a woman is not Mr *Wentworth's* home.'

'I entirely agree,' I said. 'As I happen to be a bachelor, it would be most *im*proper.'

'That is a state of affairs that could easily be remedied,' the Chairman pointed out, when the laughter had died down. 'Perhaps Miss Gorman would co-operate?'

'Oh, I'm afraid my time is very much taken up with my water-beetles, which Mr Wentworth seems so much to despise,' Miss Gorman said, with a rather tight-lipped smile. 'Somebody else must accept the honour.'

'No room for just one more?' Tallboys asked.

I enjoy the cut and thrust of debate as much as any man, but there is a point, a very definite point, at which good-humoured raillery ends and impertinence begins. Miss Coombes, who looked after the boys' vests and so on at Burgrove, put it very well, I remember, when she said 'Anyone can be clever, Etheridge, but it takes a gentleman to be courteous.' Though I said nothing, some of the annoyance I felt may very well have shown in my face. At any rate, the man in the fourth row, in whose direction I happened to be looking, hastily whipped his handkerchief up to his mouth and unless I am very much mistaken ejected whatever he was eating and put it into his pocket. Thereafter, I was glad to see he paid close attention to what was being said, and once or twice nodded his head to show agreement with some observation of my own. I know the type from of old.

A man like Tallboys, with a hide three inches thick, has to be handled differently. It is best, as a rule, to ignore them; and that is what I did. The Chairman in any case had gone on to the next question, which concerned our relations with the United States. Miss Gorman said that the future of the world depended on a close accord between the English-speaking peoples, and with this we were all agreed. Then we discussed juvenile delinquency, a subject on which I suppose I can claim to speak with some authority. Not, naturally, that there was anything serious of that kind at Burgrove, but boys are very much alike the world over and only those who have spent a lifetime in their company can hope to have a close understanding of their problems. I said that provided young people were brought up in the right way, taught to fear God and be honourable and straightforward, tell the truth and play the game in the widest sense of the phrase, we need have no fear that they would grow up in the right way. The audience took this very well, I think, and Sir Arnold backed me up by saying that a good home was the important thing. Miss Gorman talked about glands and suchlike hocus-pocus, and Tallboys said he did not think a boy was any the worse for stealing a few apples when the policeman wasn't looking. If that was how he spent his own boyhood, he is not, in my opinion, much of an advertisement for apple-stealing, but of course I did not say so. I leave cheap scores to others. The Chairman summed up, neatly enough, by saying that the panel seemed to be agreed on the whole that the younger generation would be all right provided they were taught to behave themselves.

After that we discussed interplanetary travel and mixed marriages and the best present to give a man on his fiftieth birthday. Then the Chairman announced that there were five more minutes to go and asked if any member of the audience had a question he or she would like to put. At once a woman got up and asked the extraordinary question 'Can the panel explain why there is no Request Stop at the bottom of Penfield Road, and isn't it high time something was done about it?'

Well!

I suppose it is natural, in a way, that people's small local concerns should be of more interest to them than some of the questions, many of them of fundamental importance, we had been discussing. But the immediate quickening of interest took me, I must confess, by surprise.

'Quite right, Mrs Burfitt,' somebody called out. 'Four hundred yards if it's an inch my little girl has to walk – '

'It's the shopping,' a thin woman in a beret explained. 'You don't want to trudge right up Elm Street with a heavy basket.'

'I hardly think – ' the Chairman said.

'Take Friday. There was a good half-dozen of us in all that rain, and it isn't as if you could always take your overshoes. You'd think they could do *something*.'

'*Didn't* it come down, Mrs Enticott! I saw you there, but not to speak to, being in the back, and I said to my husband "The poor thing *will* get wet, I told him – " '

'It's the same with the footpath back of the common,' a bald-headed man complained, without troubling to rise to his feet. 'You could break a leg in one of those pot-holes. It's all very well for the panel to come here and talk about mixed marriages and satellites and that, but what I'd like to know is when is something going to be done about the disgraceful state of some of our public paths?'

'Hear! Hear!' said several voices.

What astonished me was the Chairman's acquiescence in this absurd situation. He seemed perfectly content to sit back and allow the meeting to degenerate into a disorderly hubbub. Of course in a way it was no business of mine, but when a young woman got up and demanded two additional hard tennis courts in the Recreation Ground, or some such nonsense, I really could stand it no longer.

'This is not a meeting of the Rural District Council, madam,' I said. 'The panel is here, if the Chairman will allow me to say so, to answer questions of general interest, not to repair footpaths or insist on additional Request Stops – '

'But a stop at the bottom of Penfield Road *is* of general interest,' interrupted Miss Gorman, in what I am afraid was a rather obvious attempt to curry favour. 'It is certainly a matter of great interest to *me*.'

'In that case,' I replied, unable to repress a touch of sarcasm – a weapon that I am normally very loth to use, 'I shall of course make it my business to take the matter up with the bus company at the earliest possible opportunity.'

'And don't forget the footpath,' somebody called out.

These people seem to think that, just because one is on a platform, one has nothing better to do than see to all the trivial problems they are too lazy to work out for themselves. Really, one might as well be back at school.

# One Thing after Another

Word has got round that I am taking up the matter of the Penfield Road bus stop. Mrs Wheeler went out of her way to congratulate me about it this morning after church.

'We need somebody of energy and initiative in this place, Mr Wentworth,' she told me. 'There is so much to be done. It is splendid to know that you are going to interest yourself in our small concerns.'

It is absurd that a chance remark, made in a spirit of irony at a so-called 'Brains Trust', should be taken up in this literal way. But what is one to do? Mrs Wheeler would rightly have felt very rudely rebuffed had I replied that I had no intention of doing anything of the kind. Besides, I suppose in a way it is just the opportunity I have been looking for to give a helping hand here and there in Fenport. When one joins a community one has no right, even in retirement, to sit back with folded hands and expect others to do the work. 'Heaven helps those that helps theirselves' is an old adage of my nurse's that comes to mind.

I was revolving in my mind the opening phrases of a letter to the West Acre and District Transport Company, when I was hailed by Miss Stephens from the Bank. She is petite and does not, I am sure, dye her hair. Some women have a natural bronze that grows a little paler at the roots.

'Oh, Mr Wentworth,' she began in her breathless way, 'of course we hardly know each other, and I do hope you will forgive me, but the fact of the matter is it's the Dramatic Society. We are doing *The Linden Tree*, you see, it's a Priestley of course, and the old Professor – he's out of date, if you remember, and *won't* give up despite his wife's longing to get away from it all – '

'But, Miss Stephens,' I interrupted gently, 'I am rather at a loss. I shall of course be delighted to take a ticket when the time comes – '

'But we want you to *act*, Mr Wentworth,' she cried. 'It's a part that's simply made for you. So gentle, and yet so firm. I can just see you, in the big scene with Mrs Linden – '

I naturally supposed at first that she was pulling my leg.

But after a while as she prattled on, I realized that she seriously imagined I might be persuaded to go on the stage in front of half the people in Fenport and involve myself in this scene with Mrs Linden, whoever she might be. At my age! So I seized the first opportunity to tell her that I had never acted in my life, and that I feared I was a little old to begin now.

She opened her eyes very wide indeed.

'But, Mr Wentworth!' she said. 'I know that you used . . . before half the crowned heads of Europe, Mr Megrim told me.'

'Oh, Megrim!' I said.

I saw at once that this, like the bus stop business, was another result of Sidney Megrim's stupidly inept handling of the Brains Trust meeting. The next thing would be, no doubt, that somebody would ask me to give a talk to the Literary and Debating Club on Elizabethan Drama.

'Let me assure you, Miss Stephens,' I said, 'that any stories about my having once been an actor are quite unfounded. Apart from one occasion in the old days when I dressed up as Father Christmas for an end-of-term concert, I can truthfully say – '

'And what are two of my parishioners hatching up together against me now?' cried the vicar, coming up unexpectedly from behind. He has a way of taking one by the elbow that, in one not of his cloth, I should be inclined to resent. 'Something to my detriment, I'll be bound.'

Somers is a good man, with no high-church nonsense about him, but perhaps rather roguish for his years.

'You are barking up the wrong tree, Vicar,' I told him,

seeking unsuccessfully to free myself. 'I was simply explaining to Miss Stephens that, though I have dressed up as Father Christmas in my time – '

'The very man,' he interrupted. 'The very man! Now that poor old Witherby has been laid to rest. Miss Stephens, you shall persuade him. Four o'clock at the vicarage, on December the 20th. Vestments provided by the parish. Splendid, splendid. You have no idea, Wentworth, how difficult it is nowadays to get the right sort of person to take an interest in our small doings.'

'Well, really – ' I began.

'Mr Wentworth is thinking of joining our Dramatic Society,' Miss Stephens said. 'Just for a small part, perhaps, until we see how he gets on. We mustn't ask *too* much of him, must we?'

'Mine is no more than a walking-on-part, as we say,' said the vicar. 'Just a word here and there to the kiddies. A pat on the head, perhaps. You have patted heads in your time, eh, Wentworth? Four o'clock then, on the 20th of next month.'

'I very much fear,' I said – but he had darted off in his impetuous way to accost a young couple with a dachshund, and I turned to find Miss Stephens laughing gaily at me.

'*What* a breezy Christian it is,' she exclaimed. 'I always feel I ought to hold my skirts down when he's about.'

I dug the ferrule of my umbrella into the ground, at a loss for a reply.

'And hold my hat on tight and so on, I mean,' she went on with a becoming blush. 'That *was* naughty of you, about him barking up the wrong tree. I very nearly burst right out.'

'Naughty?' I said. 'In what way?'

'Don't pretend you don't know everybody calls him Frisky Fido. I should think he knows it himself, very likely.'

'Oh, that,' I said. 'Oh well.' It was the first I had heard of it, as a matter of fact, but I cannot say I was greatly surprised. The more I see of life in this neighbourhood, the more it seems to me to resemble life in a boys' preparatory school. The gossip and childishness of it all, and now nicknames for the vicar!

The only difference in a way is that there is practically no discipline.

We had quite a pleasant talk, until our ways parted at the china shop. Miss Stephens is an amusing little thing, and I should be glad to help her, within reason. But there are limits. I do not think I have committed myself about her absurd play-acting suggestion, though of course, up to a point, it might be a new experience. We shall see.

It is odd to remember that a little time ago I was complaining of a lack of useful employment here in Fenport. And now here I am, practically rushed off my feet with this Penfield Road business and rehearsals for Miss Stephens's Dramatic Society starting on Wednesday (it is really impossible to refuse so pressing a lady), not to mention the vicar's Children's Party, though that of course is not for a few weeks yet. Then there is the Vice-Presidency of the Football Club – I mean I have still to settle whether to accept the honour at a guinea a year or send them a gracefully-worded refusal. All these things mount up.

'Don't you go and do too much, Mr Wentworth,' Mrs Bretton said to me only this morning as I was on my way out to the tool-shed to straighten things up in there. 'You're too kind-hearted by far. You want to take it easy, your time of life, not run this way and that for a pack of women.' She is an excellent creature, but a little inclined to treat me as though I were an elderly invalid. 'That Miss Stephens,' she added, and would I think have said more, had I not shown by my manner that I had work to do. I do not believe in encouraging gossip, however well intentioned.

I keep my bicycle in the tool-shed, together with the mowing machine and other odds and ends. This is inconvenient at times, because of the way things have of catching in things when you want them – or rather when you don't. I mean when you don't want the things they catch in, naturally, and it is these for some tiresome reason that generally come out first when you pull. Besides, it is bad for the spokes. A lot of old paint-tins and so on were left behind by the last occupant into

the bargain, and the place needs a thorough tidy. I hate anything slipshod. The School Museum was in my charge at
Burgrove for a number of years, so I am not without experience of arranging a number of diverse objects to the best
advantage in a narrow space.

The right way to begin is to clear everything out first, and
this I proceeded to do (not, for reasons that I have explained,
without some difficulty). I shall never understand why my
predecessor here needed so much garden hose. It is awkward
stuff at the best of times, and really, for the small lawn and
two rose beds which are all I have here, one would have
thought forty feet or so would be enough. I very much doubt,
as a matter of fact, whether he ever used it at all; parts of the
middle section have clearly, to judge by the cobwebs alone,
been entangled in an old wooden rake for many years. At any
rate, after a tug or two, I decided that the only thing to do was
to unthread the hose carefully from end to end, to disengage
it, that is to say, from the various articles with which it had
become entangled. These latter could then be removed
*seriatim*.

To my astonishment, the hose appeared to have no end,
whichever way I traced it, and it was while trying to follow a
double loop through the framework of a deck-chair that I
somehow got the handle of a pair of edging shears up the left
leg of my trousers. I should not ordinarily note down the details
of so mundane an operation as tidying out a shed, but there
has been a lot of exaggerated gossip in the village – *nothing* is
too trivial, it seems, for some people – and in justice to myself
I wish to explain, quite briefly, what happened next.

Anyone who has tried to trace an unrolled garden hose, or
a tangled fishing cast for that matter, to its source knows that
it is essential at no time to lose touch. The eye is not to be
depended upon. The entire length must be followed *by hand*,
for otherwise it is all too easy to reverse one's direction un-
knowingly where two loops intersect and thus arrive back at
one's starting point. For this reason I was obliged to force my
way *through* rather than to go *round* the deck-chair, and by a
stroke of ill-luck the serrated, or notched, leg of the chair,

which happened to be uppermost, swung over on its pivots and trapped the upper part of my body. At the same time the point of the shears became jammed rather awkwardly in the lower framework – of the chair, that is – and in attempting to preserve my balance I inadvertently gave a sharpish tug to the hose (of which, I must repeat, I could not let go without throwing all my trouble to the winds) and brought down a quantity of sacking and old dahlia tubers from a shelf above my head. I was temporarily blinded. But for that I should certainly not have made what turned out to be a false move.

I suppose it may have been two or three minutes later that I heard footsteps on the gravel path outside. Not wishing to be interrupted I kept quite still, and it was with some irritation that I heard Mrs Bretton call out, rather gruffly, 'Here's Miss Stephens wants to see you, Mr Wentworth.' Still, there was nothing to be done, and a moment later I could sense that Miss Stephens was standing in the doorway.

'I'm so sorry to bother you when you are busy,' she began. Then her voice died away. 'Oh my God, Mrs Bretton!' she cried. (I suppose it is the modern way, but I do *not* like it in a woman.) 'There's something hanging up in the corner.'

The truth was that in an instinctive effort to free myself by slipping backwards through the framework of the chair and at the same time *shrugging* it, if I make myself clear, upwards, I had caught the leg-rung, by a million-to-one chance, on some nail or projection in the wall. Movement of any kind was now painful, if not positively dangerous, and it was while quietly thinking out the next step that I had become aware that I had a visitor.

'It is perfectly all right, Miss Stephens,' I said, to reassure her. 'I was looking for the end of the hose.'

'Goodness, you gave me a shock,' she said. 'It's hanging down your back.'

'Aha!' I said. 'It must have been hidden among the dahlias.'

'So are you, you poor thing,' Miss Stephens said, coming – very expertly, I must say – to my assistance.

The upshot of all this is that I have practically promised to take a part in her play. Apparently, a Wally Bishop is going abroad, and they are desperate for somebody to act the part of Lockhart, whoever *he* may be. To tell the truth, I was not in the best of tempers – nobody likes to be interrupted in the middle of a worthwhile task – and the quickest way to settle the matter seemed to be to say yes.

'In that case,' I said, 'I suppose – very well. By all means, if you wish it. Yes.'

'You *darling*!' Miss Stephens said. Of course, I know that it means nothing, among stage people, but all the same one was glad that Mrs Bretton had gone to get her husband's lunch.

The first performance is to be on December 20th, apparently. I have a feeling that I already have some engagement for that date, but Miss Stephens says it doesn't matter. I don't know, I'm sure, whether I have been altogether wise.

# The Penfield Road Affair

A man named Willis, who is something to do with the Gas
Company I believe, called about the H-bomb this morning. He
told me that sheep were eating grass coated with Strontium 90,
or some such number, and wanted me to protest about it.

'This is all a little bit outside my province,' I told him. I
know nothing about sheep, and was in any case rather busy.

'Is the extermination of the whole human race outside your
province, then?' he asked.

'It is certainly more than I have time for this morning,' I
said, ignoring the rudeness of his manner. 'At the moment I
have my hands full with this business of a Request Stop at the
bottom of Penfield Road. Perhaps, while you are here, you
would care to join in a protest against the intransigent attitude
of the bus company? Only a few days ago, I am told – '

He seemed to be a man without any sense of proportion.
'Penfield Road!' he cried. 'A fat lot it will matter whether the
buses stop at Penfield Road or anywhere else when there's
nobody left to ride in them and the whole of Europe is a
desolate waste. It's people like you, with their noses buried in
their own petty little local affairs, that are bringing the world
to the brink of destruction. Can't you realize that already seaweed is being dredged up with point nought six of a fatal dose
of radiation in it? And you talk about bus stops!'

I am not the man to be hectored on my own doorstep.

'Listen to me, young man,' I said. 'When I was your age
there were plenty of people going about saying that the end of
the world was at hand. They used to hold meetings, I remember, with the slogan "Millions Now Living Will Never
Die". A fine state we should all have been in if I had listened

to them and decided it was not worth while to go on teaching my boys trigonometry. Get on with your own job, my lad, and leave sheep and seaweed to wiser heads.' For two pins I would have told him to get his hair cut and take his bicycle-clips off before calling uninvited at strange houses. I did, in fact, say something of the kind, more or less *sotto voce*, and he went away muttering.

I had meant to get a strong letter off to the bus company (or the *Advertiser* perhaps would be better), but this Willis interview unsettled me and after thinking things over for an hour or two I set off to change a book at the library. Mrs Wheeler was there, half-way up a ladder, and we chatted for a while.

'I feel like Romeo and Juliet,' she said. 'Why not come and have dinner one evening, Mr Wentworth? On Friday week? One or two people will be there whom you might like to meet, if you haven't met them already.'

'I'm sure I shall be delighted to meet them even if I *have* met them already,' I said politely. I had not intended any joke, but Mrs Wheeler began to laugh so I joined in.

'That would depend, wouldn't it?' she said. 'Suppose I asked Mr Willis?'

'Willis!' I said. 'You mean the gas man!'

'He says you threw his bicycle-clips in his face. I must say it doesn't sound very likely, but he *did* seem angry. Of course, he did not say it to me, but they were outside Gooch's just now and I couldn't very well help hearing. Then that man Odding –'

'Odding?'

'Yes. They were talking, you see. Odding said nothing would surprise him. He said you rang his wife up the other day and threatened to pelt her with carrots. There was something else, but I had my shopping to do, and of course –'

'This is getting beyond a joke,' I broke in angrily. 'If those two men are getting together to spread slanderous stories about me I shall certainly take action. The whole thing is a mare's nest. I simply rang up Mrs Odding to explain that if she heard any silly stories about my – about carrots being thrown at her

at the greengrocer's it was all a misunderstanding. She is unfortunately an Estonian – '

'But, Mr Wentworth, surely even an Estonian would know
whether she was or was not being pelted with carrots. I mean
if it wasn't true, I don't quite see – '

'Exactly,' I said. 'The carrots have been trumped up against
me by ill-disposed gossips. There were a few on the floor, not
more than a few, and nobody was hurt. Actually, the whole
thing started with a lettuce.'

'You threw a lettuce at Mrs Odding?'

'I neither threw, nor threatened to throw, anything at anybody, Mrs Wheeler. I merely gave vent to an expression at the
greengrocer's – '

'Muriel!' Mrs Wheeler called out suddenly. 'Mr Wentworth is telling me how he gave vent to an expression at the
greengrocer's.'

I had not noticed Miss Stephens come into the library. She
now joined us with an 'Oh, do tell!' and the two ladies listened
sympathetically while I gave a short account of the circumstances that had led me to make a hasty remark in Wrightson's
shop about Mrs Odding's order for lettuces, and how my
attempt to apologize to the woman on the telephone had been
misinterpreted by her fool of a husband. 'The whole thing is a
storm in a tea-cup,' I ended.

'I don't suppose you really threw Willis's cycle-clips in his
face either,' Mrs Wheeler commented.

'Oh *no*?' Miss Stephens cried. 'Mr Wentworth, you really
*are*!'

I explained that the man had no doubt been speaking
figuratively. 'I may be old-fashioned,' I said, 'but I would
never dream of going to anybody's front door without removing my bicycle-clips, and I do not expect people to come to
mine without removing theirs. All the same, I should have said
nothing, of course, if the man had been civil. Standing there
lecturing me about seaweed and decrying the Request Stop,
when I am old enough to be his father, though I am bound to
say that I should have to be a *great* deal older before I would
dream – however, that is neither here nor there. The man was

uncivil, and I sent him away with a flea in his ear, as my old nurse used to say.'

Both ladies were blowing their noses, and there was a short silence.

'I'm sure he richly deserved it,' Mrs Wheeler said. 'He was rude about the – about the Request Stop, you say?'

'I thought he would be better employed in joining me in a protest about the Penfield Road business than in badgering people with a lot of nonsense about radioactive sheep. "Get your hair cut," I told him, "and leave all that tomfoolery to wiser heads".'

'That settled *him*, I should think,' Mrs Wheeler said. 'But I *am* so glad you are taking the Request Stop so seriously. And what a splendid idea to organize a protest!'

'Hardly that. Hardly that, dear lady,' I said. 'I am merely writing a letter to the *Advertiser*, which I think will do some good.'

'I certainly mustn't miss *that*,' Miss Stephens said.

Their interest and enthusiasm encouraged me to go straight home and write a fairly stiff letter to the local paper, without further delay. It will make the West Acre and Fenport Transport Company sit up, I fancy.

This Penfield Road bus-stop affair is becoming more of a nuisance than it is worth. A day or two after posting my letter to the *Advertiser* it occurred to me to walk out and see the actual terrain, what was involved in the way of distances between existing stops, etc. 'Get out into the field, Wentworth,' my old C.O. used to say to me in the last war, and though I never quite became used to being spoken to as if I were a horse, I am sure his advice was sound. An ounce of knowledge is worth a deal of theory, as they say.

It was a considerable shock to me to find that there is already a Request Stop at Penfield Road. I can only suppose that the bus company had got wind of the fact that the matter was being taken up by someone who was not likely to be put off by excuses and evasions, and had decided to anticipate what they knew to be an unanswerable demand. I felt very badly let

down, and my first thought was, of course, to withdraw the
letter I had written to the *Advertiser*. This meant fourpence in
a telephone kiosk which I can ill afford.

'I wrote you a letter the day before yesterday,' I said as soon
as I was through. 'About the Request Stop at Penfield – '

'Do you want Basting?' a voice said.

'Certainly not,' I replied. 'I wish the letter to be withdrawn
immediately. It must not appear.'

'You want the Editor then,' the voice said. 'Only he's out.'

'Who is that?' I asked sharply. 'I must speak to the Editor.
This is a matter of the utmost – '

'Mr Basting's gone, see? If it's about the letter, it's in. This
is Partridge 'ere, the boy, and it'll be out Friday.'

'No, no,' I said. 'It must come out *now*! The letter must not
appear. I am speaking from Penfield Road, and the fact is that
a bus stop has recently been installed. That being so – '

'We knew that, o' course,' the boy said.

'Then naturally you will not print my letter, which was
written in ignorance of the facts.'

'It's in,' he repeated. 'On the machines. "It'll stir up correspondence, anyway," Mr Basting said. "There'll be plenty
of people glad enough to point out the error," he said. He said
we don't get a letter putting its foot in it right up to the neck
*every* week, he said. "And what's more," he said – '

Never, even in my schoolmastering days (except perhaps in
the matter of the changing-room pegs in Poole's time) have I
met so utterly irresponsible an attitude. 'Listen to me, Partridge,' I said. 'I think you are mistaking your man. You may
tell your Editor from me that if my letter is printed I shall not
hesitate to write him another, which he will not like. He has
no business to include correspondence, written as I say, in
ignorance of the facts – '

'Look,' the boy had the impertinence to reply, 'if we cut out
letters just because they were written in ignorance of the facts,
we wouldn't *have* no correspondence. "Bung it in," Mr Basting
said to me – '

I was not prepared, of course, to listen to this kind of talk.
'Bung it in,' indeed! Sometimes I wonder what the world is

coming to, when young flippertigibbets, scarcely out of their teens to judge by their voices, can speak in that strain to a man old enough to have forgotten more than they ever learnt. If this is what comes of trying to give a helping hand to the people of this village they will soon find that they have a very different kettle of fish to deal with. It is all very well to pester me to dress up as Father Christmas next December and have this extraordinary scene with Mrs Linden, if that was the name, and do this that and the other thing, but if all I am to get in return is a lot of inaccurate gossip about throwing carrots, at *my* age, and now this trouble with the *Advertiser*, I might as well go back to Burgrove and try to hammer a bit of sense into a lot of boys who, with all their faults, never dreamed of using strong language in my presence. There is such a thing as flogging a dead horse, as I shall tell them.

# The Party at the Vicarage

It has been a trying day, and might well have ended in a contretemps. But as I have often found in life, difficulties and
mishaps are there to be overcome, and if faced with calmness
and common sense sometimes turn out to be all for the best.
Looking back on it all, I cannot feel that there is anything to
regret, though of course another year, before agreeing to give
away the presents at the Vicarage Christmas Party, I shall
make certain that it does not clash with the opening night of
the Dramatic Society's play – assuming (as I am bold enough
to do) that Miss Stephens will again ask me to take a part.
Dashing from one engagement to another, for all the world as
if I were a Prime Minister or some such functionary, is a bit
too much of a good thing at my time of life.

Things would have run more smoothly, I dare say, but for
a muddle over my Father Christmas outfit. This was no fault
of mine, for I was in good time at the Vicarage and naturally
expected to find everything ready for me there. It was quite a
shock when Mrs Somers greeted me, almost before I had got
my bicycle-clips off, with a cry of 'But where are your *things*?'
She told me that they had been sent round to my house so that
I could try them on, get used to the feel of the beard and so on
– 'We always did that in poor Witherby's time,' she said, as
though that had anything to do with it – and what she could
*not* understand was how I had failed to see the parcel.

'Naturally I saw the parcel, Mrs Somers,' I replied. 'At least,
I saw *a* parcel that somebody must have left on my doorstep
when I was out. But I am afraid I am old-fashioned enough,

when parcels come for me at this season, not to open them until Christmas Day.'

Mrs Somers threw up her hands in a gesture that, considering the circumstances, I found somewhat irritating. 'The children will be bitterly disappointed,' she said. 'We had hoped that you would be ready to greet them when they arrived, and – Oh dear! Here comes Mrs Thompson already with her two. *What* are we to do?'

Well, I have faced worse crises many a time in the old days, without losing my head as Mrs Somers seemed to have done. I shall not forget in a hurry the time the under-Matron came back from a wedding in a very strained state, and I had to make an immediate decision whether to send the boys out on a run or order them into the gymnasium for extra P.T. It would have been better, as it turned out, to send them for a run; but the important thing, as I explained to the Headmaster, was to get them out of the way quickly, not to stand about debating the pros and cons. I could not possibly know that Miss Vincent would herself go straight to the gym to sleep it off. There was the occasion, too, when the chapel organ became waterlogged on Confirmation Sunday – but there is no need to go into all that now. My point is that an old schoolmaster is not likely to be thrown out of his stride by a temporary hitch at a children's party.

'Surely, Mrs Somers,' I said quietly, 'it will be more effective if I arrive *after* the children are assembled? As though by sleigh. It will take me no more than twenty minutes to ride home, collect the parcel and return.'

'They will see you arriving,' she said. 'They are as sharp as needles.'

'It will be dark,' I replied. 'What is more, to be on the safe side, I will put on the costume before approaching the house. I do not see, in that case that it will matter even if – '

'Oh, Mr Wentworth!' she cried. 'Without a sack, and wheeling a bicycle! The children would be bitterly – '

'Then what do you suggest, madam?' I asked, very nearly at the end of my patience.

She bit her lip. 'Perhaps, if you wouldn't mind,' she said –

'Here comes Mrs Whitney's little boy, in tears already – if you would come in by the side gate when you get back? Down the lane here, and up through the garden to the conservatory door. You would be out of sight from the front, you see, and we could give you the sack – '

'Give me the sack, eh?' I put in. 'There's gratitude for you!' But she was too fussed to appreciate the joke, and with an abrupt 'I must fly!' went off into the house.

I found when I got home that the parcel, mainly because of the top-boots, was too bulky to be carried on my bicycle, so there was nothing for it but to ride back to the Vicarage in full Father Christmas rig. The beard I could of course have strapped to the carrier or thrust into an inside pocket, but after some hesitation I put it on. It would be better, I thought, in case I were seen on the journey, not to be too readily recognizable.

I have had little or no experience of bicycling in fancy dress, and after one or two unsuccessful attempts to mount in the normal manner I realized that it would be necessary to pull the cloak up about my waist. I therefore gathered the skirts and had raised them with some difficulty as far as my knees when a voice called out 'Oh! Oh!', adding as it receded into the dusk, 'Time for another Request Stop agitation.' I could not see the face of the passer-by who made this senseless remark, but I have reason to believe that it was Willis, of the Gas Company, a man I have never liked. He has some bee in his bonnet about saving the world from annihilation, but would be better advised in my opinion to start by mending his manners. At any rate I made no reply and once I had learned the trick of turning the toes of my top boots outwards to avoid fouling the front mudguard was soon on my way. I dare say some of my Burgrove boys would have been surprised if they could have seen their old master pedalling along in a white beard, with a red cloak tucked up round his knees; but I have never been afraid to do something a little out of the ordinary, I think I may claim, particularly if it is to save kiddies from disappointment.

The journey, as a matter of fact, was uneventful (though I

thought I heard some silly giggling as I turned into Dyson Road), and I reached the Vicarage without accident. The front of the house was ablaze with lights, but the lane itself was very dark, which made it a matter of some difficulty to find the side gate. Still, it was not many minutes before I was safely inside the garden and, leaving my bicycle by the hedge, began to make my way cautiously up a narrow gravel path.

It would have been a kindness had Mrs Somers thought of posting somebody with a light to guide me in, and I can only suppose that her anxiety not in any way to disappoint the children led her to neglect this small attention. The result was that I must have branched off the direct route to the house and, after fruitless knocking, entered a greenhouse, which I naturally took to be the conservatory. I suppose I must have taken half a dozen steps before the strong smell of damp earth, the heat of the place (excessive for December), and the complete absence of light combined to make me realize my mistake. I immediately turned round, though not apparently through a hundred and eighty degrees, and stepped into a cactus – an awkward enough customer even for an unbearded man. This mishap made me, I am ashamed to say, momentarily lose my composure, and in wrenching myself free I incautiously stepped backwards off the duck-boards, lost my balance and toppled, rather than fell, into a trough or container of some soft flour-like substance, which the vicar told me later was horticultural soot.

Like most men who have led a busy active life I have once or twice before found myself at a loss in dark confined spaces, and experience has taught me the vital importance of standing absolutely still. Not indefinitely of course, but long enough to allow the mind to formulate a plan of campaign. On this occasion I adopted the same course, and very soon decided that I had only to regain the duck-boards and, keeping my left foot in contact with their edge, follow them to the door. Sure enough, some half-dozen paces brought me to the end, and extending my right hand I was greatly relieved to find it in contact with what must be the handle of the door. To this I gave a half-turn, and was at once aware of a fine but persistent jet or spray of water which seemed to come at me from every direction. The explanation, that I ought of course to have kept my *right* foot in contact with the duck-boards, did not immediately occur to me, and I fear that I did some little damage in my anxiety to be gone, before I understood that I was now at the wrong end of the greenhouse. Thinking back over the incident I am inclined to agree that my wisest step, after that first instinctive leap backwards, would have been to search again for the controlling handle or tap and turn the water off. But men do not always, in emergency, do the wisest thing. What I very much resent is the suggestion that I at any time panicked or lost my head. The simple fact that, when on my way back down the greenhouse, I kept the soot-trough constantly in mind and on this occasion disentangled myself from the cactus with proper deliberation should be enough to scotch *that* snake.

That I was vexed and put out by the whole business I do not deny. Indeed, when I regained the dry open air my intention was to return straight home, however bitter the disappointment might be to the kiddies, and it was pure chance that led my footsteps to the conservatory instead of to my bicycle. Having got so far, however, I thought it my duty to let some member of the household know that I was unfortunately unable to give away the presents as arranged. Accordingly I made my way through the back portions of the house, where I saw nobody except a woman working at a sink, who gave a shrill cry as soon as I accosted her and locked herself into a cupboard. I have no patience at all with female hysterics and simply passed on into the hall, which was brightly lit and gaily decorated with streamers and balloons. From a closed door leading, as I knew, into the dining-room came the sound of youthful voices and the clatter of tea-cups, but the hall itself was empty, and it was while pondering what best to do that I happened to catch sight of my reflection in a large and, to my mind, rather rococo looking-glass.

I at once decided that my best plan, after all, would be to go quietly home and telephone from there. One is prepared, of course, to look odd, even ridiculous, in the garb of Father

Christmas, but I was certainly not prepared to present myself in company in the state to which I was now, through no fault of my own, reduced. The gown itself was not seriously torn, except about the hem, but my face was so mottled and streaked with soot and perspiration that I do not believe even my old colleagues would have recognized me. Rivulets of blackened water had run down the full length of my beard, which was sadly awry. My hands, naturally enough, were coated with soot and dried blood (a good mixture I remember thinking – so oddly does the mind associate in times of stress – for brussels sprouts). There was leaf-mould not only on my boots but even on my scarlet hood, and twined about my right sleeve was some kind of creeper with curious fleshy leaves.

It was in trying, with an understandable gust of annoyance, to shake or flick this last encumbrance from me that my right-hand came by ill-luck into contact with an old-fashioned gong immediately behind me. A low resonant boom rang through the house, and I had scarcely time to take one quick step towards the front door when the dining-room door was thrown open and Somers himself stood framed in the aperture.

'St Chrysostom!' he said.

My first concern was to assure him that the sounding of the gong had been purely accidental. One does not, naturally, summon people intentionally in such a way – least of all in their own homes.

'I was flicking off a creeper –' I began.

'Flicking off a creeper!' he repeated, in the voice of a man who attaches little or no meaning to what he is saying. 'My dear fel – Not you, Jackie. Get back, boy, and shut the door.'

He was too late, however. A little red-haired boy, who belongs I think to the butcher, peered round his legs and set up a cry of 'He's come! He's here! Father Christmas is come down the chimley!' At once there was a rush from within the room, and a cluster of boys and girls pushed and jostled their way into the doorway. I realized that it would never do, whatever my personal vexation, to forget the part I was supposed to be playing. Accordingly, I did my best to smile cheerily at the youngsters, and gave them a welcoming wave of one of my blackened and bleeding hands. 'Merry Christmas!' I said.

One or two of the smaller ones started to cry, but I very soon put an end to that.

'Stop that noise this instant!' I ordered, and there was an immediate silence. I have not been a schoolmaster for thirty-five years for nothing – little though it was that I got, in another sense, I am bound to say.

Mrs Somers had by this time worked her way to the front of the group, and I heard the vicar tell her, still in the same low bemused voice 'All he *says* is that he was flicking off a creeper.' It was a difficult situation for her, in some ways, as for me. But she is a well-bred woman, and her years of training as a hostess told her instinctively what to do.

'Perhaps, dear,' she said briskly, 'Father Christmas would like a wash.'

'Of course, of course,' the vicar said, coming forward while his lady began to shepherd her charges back into the dining-room.

'What on earth, Wentworth?' he went on, when the door was safely shut. 'My dear fellow, you are all wet, apart from the – Where have you *been*?'

'I have been in your greenhouse,' I said shortly.

'In my green – ? To shelter from the rain? I had no idea – '

'Not to shelter,' I said, and there was something in my voice that warned him, I think, that I did not wish to pursue the matter at present.

'Come along, anyhow,' he cried. 'Come along and wash. This way, this way. Mind the gong.'

'I am neither blind nor incapable, thank you,' I said irritably. 'It was by pure mischance that I had my back turned when shaking or flicking – '

'Shaking or flicking?' he said. 'Dear me! I hardly know – ' He has a tiresome habit of rushing into speech before one has fairly begun what one has to say. 'By the *way*,' he added, halting suddenly in front of a door, 'I suppose when you had – er finished in the greenhouse, you remembered to shut the door?'

'I doubt very much,' I replied, 'whether it makes any difference now whether the door is shut or open.' I did not, to tell the truth, very much care.

'My calceolarias!' he cried – or some such ridiculous expletive. 'In that case – in here, please. Forgive me!' And he was off, leaving me to tidy up as best I might in peace.

Well, it had been an unlucky business in many ways. But misfortunes, as I have said, can sometimes be turned to good account. The children were not at all frightened when I finally entered the room carrying a laden sack. Indeed they clustered about me, demanding to know what it was like coming down a chimney; which one I had chosen; where my reindeer were, and suchlike childish questions. 'You really made the tiny ones *believe* in Father Christmas again,' Mrs Somers told me later on. 'You see, they had got rather too used to poor old Witherby. I do think it was clever of you to think of the soot.'

'Yes, yes. Yes, indeed,' Somers said. 'Though I could wish – if you had thought of asking – however, there it is.'

I thought it best to leave it at that for the time being. Everybody was most kind, and even when I gave little Felicity Bennings a pat on the head and a quantity of soot, which must have somehow lodged in my sleeve, fell on her flaxen curls, the incident passed off with general good humour. There were games and crackers, and really, despite my damp gown, the years seemed to roll away. It was quite a disappointment when people began to leave. I was playing 'Puss in the Corner' – at my age! – when Mrs Somers came running from the telephone to say that I was wanted at once at the Parish Hall.

'It's Miss Stephens,' she said. 'She says the curtain goes up in ten minutes, and where on earth have you got to?'

'God bless my soul!' I cried. 'The play! I had forgotten all about it.'

# The Play

I hardly know how the play happened to escape my memory, except, of course, that I was late at the Vicarage on account of the imbroglio in the greenhouse and one thing and another. Goodness knows it has been in my mind often enough the last few weeks, with rehearsals three days a week, and now one of my two arm-chairs borrowed for scenery. I am to be Alfred Lockhart, who comes in first and says 'Oh – I say, is this right?' not the Professor. Lockhart is described in the directions – the play we are doing is, of course, *The Linden Tree*, by a man called Priestley, about whom I know little though I remember once reading what seemed to me a very much too highly-coloured account of life in a preparatory school by a man of the same name – at any rate Lockhart is described as 'a precise, anxious, clerkly, middle-aged man', which made me chuckle when I read it. 'Hardly the part for me, Miss Stephens,' I pointed out; but she said she was sure I could do it very nicely. I suppose that is the point of acting, in a way. To be somebody different, I mean. If we all went on the stage to play ourselves it would be just like everyday life, which nobody wants to pay half a crown to see, I take it, or even a shilling farther back.

I dare say Sidney Megrim has had a lot of experience in producing, as we call it, but his manner is sometimes a little, well, abrupt, considering the difference in our ages. It is not after all as if one were being *paid* to make onself out to be 'precise and anxious' and all the rest of it – as is the case, for instance, when a younger Headmaster (*mutatis mutandis*, naturally) takes advantage of his position to administer a rebuff. At the very first reading of the play I had no sooner said this opening line about 'Oh, I say, is this all right?' (We were not in costume then, of course – strictly speaking: though as a matter of fact I wear an ordinary suit when we are – but even so I held up both hands as I spoke, to show surprise and doubt) – I had no sooner spoken than Megrim interrupted with a quite gratuitous 'No, it is *not* all right, Wentworth. It's terrible.'

'Indeed?' I said. 'And in what precise manner – '

'Look,' he said. 'You have just been shown into the room by Mrs Cotton here – '

'By Miss Stephens,' I corrected.

'By Miss Stephens, if you prefer it, who is taking the part of Mrs Cotton, woman-of-all-work to the Linden household. Right? You have come to see Mrs Linden. You expected therefore to be shown into the drawing-room. You find your-self in Professor Linden's study. Right? What's the good of gabbling off your opening line and *then* looking surprised? Come in. Look round the room. Register surprise – "Oh!" – and off you go.'

'You mean exit?' I asked. 'At once?'

'Off you go with your speech, man. Now try it again, there's a good chap.'

I said nothing, but at once, as a good trouper should, did my best to follow his instructions by looking round the room – St Mark's Hall, of course, actually – with growing astonish-ment.

'Get on with it, man!' Megrim said. 'You haven't come to take an inventory of the furniture.'

It is almost impossible to get the feel of a part if one is to be constantly interrupted.

'I have been shown in a good many wrong rooms in my time, young man,' I began –

'I dare say,' he said. 'But not into this one. Again, please.'

I kept my temper, of course. As Miss Stephens said later, it is all part of the game. 'You did it splendidly, Mr Wentworth,' she told me. 'Sidney only makes us go through it over and over again because it helps to fix the lines in one's memory.'

'I see,' I said. 'Yes. I hadn't thought of that.'

When the telephone call came through to the Vicarage to say that the play was due to begin in a few minutes it was a considerable shock to me. I am a firm believer in punctuality, and of course it is most important that all the actors should be present on the opening night of a new play. New to Fenport, that is; the play has already, I understand, been performed elsewhere. But by a stroke of luck a Mrs Downing offered me a lift in her motor to the Parish Hall, and I climbed in, still in the Santa Claus outfit in which I had been helping to entertain the children. There would be time enough to change when I got to the Hall. At least, not time enough exactly, but one knows what one means. The important thing was to get there without delay, and I am afraid I cried out a little impatiently when one of Mrs Downing's youngsters went back into the house for a missing balloon. 'It was a *red* one' the boy kept saying, as if that mattered. Children have very little sense of proportion at times.

Megrim was standing at the back, or I suppose I should say 'stage' door, and addressed me at once, characteristically without bothering to say good evening.

'My God!' he said. 'Where have you *been*? We've had to ring up.'

'I know that,' I replied, overlooking the blasphemy. 'I was at the Vicarage when the call came. I am sorry, but – '

'The curtain, man, the curtain!' he cried. 'Muriel Stephens is on now, dusting round and gagging. They got impatient. Get on as quick as you can and never mind the make-up.'

'At once!' I cried, and ran past him through the dressing-room.

I cannot think how I came to forget that I was still wearing the absurd red gown and rather soot-stained beard in which I had passed the earlier part of the evening. Looking back on it, I suppose the rush, and my anxiety not to keep Miss Stephens and the audience waiting, momentarily disturbed my judge-ment. One must remember, too, that I was already 'in costume' and so not unnaturally felt ready to 'go on'. Even a more experienced actor, I dare say, might become confused if he had to rush at a moment's notice from one engagement to another.

I do not acquit myself entirely from blame, but as a fair-minded man I consider it was part of Megrim's duty, as producer, to say a word of warning about my clothing. Be that as it may, I lost no time in making my entry and, after adjusting my eyes to the glare of the footlights and taking a quick look round the stage, as instructed at rehearsal, repeated my opening line.

'Oh, I say,' I said, 'is this right?'

Of course, strictly, I should have been shown in by Miss Stephens, or 'Mrs Cotton' to give her her stage name, but as she was already there, dusting and so on, that could not be helped. In any case as it turned out, it did not matter. Miss Stephens turned round, duster in hand, and instead of replying with *her* opening speech (which runs, as a matter of fact, 'Right? It's as right as we can make it. Nothing's right now, nor ever will be, if you ask me,' and so can hardly be described as difficult to memorize), simply stood and gaped. No doubt she was surprised by my appearance, but as an actress of considerable experience – however, there it was. The audience had broken into loud laughter immediately on my opening line, so it may be that, even if she had taken her cue, she would not have been heard.

The situation was a difficult one for both of us. The laughter grew in volume and I felt completely bewildered. I am no stranger to merriment, for a schoolmaster's life is by no means the dull and colourless affair that some people make it out to be, nor am I without the means of quelling it when it threatens to grow beyond bounds. But on this occasion I felt quite at a loss – until happening to put my hand up to my chin, as is my habit when puzzled or upset, I encountered my beard and at once became aware how incongruous my costume must appear in a modern play, even at Christmas time. It was difficult to know what to do for the best. Somebody off-stage was shouting 'Come off the stage, you fool!' which did not help. But what particularly distressed me was to catch sight of Mrs Wheeler, a lady whom I respect and admire, sitting in the front row and looking over her handkerchief at me with eyes that, unless I

am much mistaken, were filled with tears. To her, at 'east, I felt
that some explanation was due.

'I was unfortunately delayed, Mrs Wheeler,' I began, stepping forward to the footlights. 'There was a slight imbroglio in
the Vicarage greenhouse – '

I got no further, partly because I saw that Mrs Wheeler was
doubled up as though in pain, and partly because at this point
somebody, Megrim I suppose, pulled the curtains across and I
had much ado to avoid becoming seriously entangled in the
folds. So that was that.

We rang up again, as the saying goes, about ten minutes
later, after Megrim had made a short speech to fill in the time
while I was busy changing and making up. It all went off very
well, I think. It was a little awkward, naturally, to have to
repeat my opening line, with which the audience were by now
familiar, but I carried it off by varying the intonation.

'Oh, I *say*!' I said. 'Is *this* right?'

'Well, it's better,' some fool at the back called out (I suspect
Willis), and there was renewed laughter; but neither Miss
Stephens nor I took any notice, and after waiting for the noise
to subside, went quietly on with the play. I must say, everybody
seemed to enjoy it. I make no claim to be an actor, but I confess
there were tears in my own eyes during my final scene with
Professor Linden (actually Major Thorpe, from West Acre),
when we discuss the need for colour and vision in education.
How true that is! Major Thorpe I thought excellent. So indeed
were all the others, and it was a real surprise to me at the end
to hear my own name called out first of all. The proper thing,
of course, as the author was not present, would have been to
call upon the Major, or possibly the producer, to take a bow. I
took no notice therefore, affecting not to hear; but the shout
was taken up in all parts of the hall, and the clamour eventually reached such proportions that I was reluctantly forced to
step forward and raise a hand to stop it.

'Ladies and gentlemen,' I said, when I was able to make
myself heard, 'I am at a loss to know why I am singled out in
this way. This is my first appearance on any stage – or rather,'

I added with a smile, 'in a sense my second, as a gentleman at the back has just reminded me. I hope it will not be my last.'

'So do we,' cried Miss Stephens: a remark which was greeted with such prolonged and good-humoured applause that I found it by no means easy, hardened as I am to such scenes by innumerable Prize-givings and so on, to restrain my emotion.

'It has been a great privilege,' I continued, 'to learn some of the elements of this great art in the company of so gifted and distinguished a – er – cast. To Miss Stephens, who first enlisted my aid in this enterprise; to our indefatigable producer, Mr Sidney Megrim; to Major Thorpe, for whose performance tonight I feel sure the knowledgeable and incisive dramatic critic of the *Advertiser* will find the right word, if right word there be; to Miss Edge, but for whose painstaking make-up – '

I had intended to conclude the list of those who had helped in one way or another with the production by adding 'to all these I owe a debt that I can never hope to repay,' or some such suitable, and indeed sincere, phrase. But the applause and clapping that followed each name as I mentioned it was so enthusiastic that I fear I lost the thread of my own remarks. Indeed, during the particularly prolonged (and I am sure well-deserved) burst of cheering occasioned by my reference to Miss Edge, our make-up artist, my mind unaccountably wandered to the earlier part of the evening and I was unable to restrain an involuntary exclamation of dismay.

'God bless my soul!' I cried. 'I left my bicycle at the Vicarage.'

There was so much laughter at this – in which, after a momentary bewilderment, I readily joined – that I thought it best to leave the matter where it rested and give way to Megrim, who took the opportunity to say a few words of thanks on his own behalf.

So ended a memorable evening. Everybody has been more than kind, especially to one who took, after all, only a comparatively minor part. Even Odding, a man whom I have perhaps judged too hastily, came up to tell me that I had given him the best evening of his life. I am too old a hand to take such exaggerated praise at more than its face value. Still, there is no denying that kindness, as one gets on in life, is very warming.

One has much to be thankful for. It has been a tiring day, not without moments of difficulty that might easily, but for a certain – 'knack', shall I call it? – that only years and experience can bestow, have ended in disaster. But the ending has been a happy one. I feel that I am beginning to take a full part, a rewarding part, in the life of the village that is now my home. One does not want to become sentimental, but I think I may claim that I am 'accepted' in Fenport, that I belong. And that, to an old man who has sometimes been lonely, means much.

My mind is at rest, what is more, about my bicycle. The vicar rang up to say that he had stumbled across it by his garden gate and had put it in the greenhouse for the night. So it is, in his own rather odd phrase 'more or less under cover'.

# A Disappointing Start

It is not easy for a retired schoolmaster to live in the manner to which he is accustomed (and *that* is no great shakes, in all conscience) on a small pension and the few shillings saved from a lifetime spent trying to knock the elementary principles of mathematics into a succession of thick-headed Burgrove boys. One does not expect, naturally, to be able to afford television sets and all the other fal-lals that I am told are now necessities – necessities, forsooth! – for millions of people who have never heard of Pythagoras and could not solve a second-degree equation to save their lives, but a man likes a pipe of tobacco now and again, and really there are times when one hardly knows where to turn with collar-attached shirts coming back in a parlous condition from the laundry at one-and-fourpence a time and baked beans, which I do *not* like, almost a luxury now. Something ought to be done, though it is hard to say what. I certainly have no intention of accepting charity, from the Government or anyone else, at my time of life. Not that I would have accepted it as a young man, I need hardly say.

All that, however, is beside the point. I am not in my dotage yet by any manner of means, and prefer to plough my own furrow so long as I have my health and strength. My hearing is remarkably good, considering, and as to my eyesight not much escapes me, as Mrs Bretton found to her cost only the other day when she forgot to dust behind the clock. At the same time I do not altogether care for the idea of taking some fiddling coaching or tutoring job down here in Fenport, where I have other interests and, perhaps I may say without immodesty, a certain standing. The answer for a man in my position seems to me to be some form of part-time occupation elsewhere, it might be as companion or adviser to some young man or family, just for two or three months in the year. I fancy, with my experience, I could be of some assistance in any one of a number of situations that come to mind – and I use the word 'situation' in its widest sense, of course. One has not held the post of Headmaster's right-hand man (which I think I may say I was in my later years at Burgrove, despite young Rawlinson's tendency at times to – well, push himself forward a little more than his qualifications or attainments warranted) without acquiring the administrative ability and, shall we say, *savoir faire* that could be of inestimable value in, for instance, arranging a tour abroad, buying tickets and so on, or in taking charge of whatever it might be while others were temporarily absent. That kind of thing. Difficulties constantly arise, as I well know, where there is need for someone absolutely trustworthy to take over until matters sort themselves out. At any rate, we shall see.

Retired schoolmaster, B.A. (Oxon) wd consider short-term employment, up to 3 mths if interesting work. Posns of trust, organization, etc. Willing to travel, within limits. Accustomed sole charge individuals or gps. No agencies or divorce work.

I should not myself have thought it necessary to make the final provision, particularly in an advertisement for insertion in *The Times*, but an old friend whom I consulted on this matter tells me that it is advisable, if one wishes to avoid unpleasant entanglements. I am not exactly certain what 'No agencies' means, as a matter of fact, but I can well believe that it is something I should not care to be mixed up in. One hears of detective agencies, for instance. I can put my finger on the guilty party as promptly as any man when it is a matter of paper-dart-throwing or that bizarre business of Matron's overshoes, and I dare say the knowledge of human nature one acquires as a schoolmaster would stand me in good stead if I were ever called upon to investigate more serious crimes. I had no doubt whatever in my own mind about the theft of Miss Stevens's ducks down here the other week. Foxes, indeed! 'That was a two-legged fox, if ever I saw one,' I told her, and would very soon have named the culprit had she not already been paid compensation by the Hunt secretary. Still, that was all in the way of friendship. It is a very different matter to stand about in shrubberies at so much the hour and jot down the numbers of young men who arrive in Jaguars. The numbers of their cars, that is to say. I shall certainly decline any offers of work of that kind.

One will have to feel one's way. Who knows? Perhaps by this time next week I shall be far away from my little cottage in Fenport, engaged in some employment of a confidential nature. The years seem to roll away. One is on the threshold of, if not adventure at least a change. That is the great thing. I might almost be a young man again, eagerly awaiting the start of my first term as an assistant master. We shall see, as I have already said.

There have been no replies as yet to my advertisement, apart from a suggestion that I might be interested in investing £200 in a second-hand furniture shop shortly about to open in South Wales. I am not. I have not put aside fifty pounds a year from my earnings ever since I was twenty-five in order to provide Welshmen with dressers and mahogany chests-of-drawers. Other considerations apart, I know nothing about second-hand furniture shops except that I have yet to see a customer enter one. I remember, years ago, asking a colleague why it was that such shops always kept half their furniture outside on the pavement, but he did not know. He said it was the same with people who sold ladders and enamelled baths. 'But not butchers or chemists,' I objected, and he agreed. One would have thought there would be by-laws.

My copy of *The Burgrovian* arrived by the same post as this extraordinary suggestion and I was skimming through 'Notes and News' (young Phillips has been playing hockey for Sandhurst, I see, though they have got his second initial wrong again) when an odd thought made me smile. 'Mr A. J. Wentworth's many friends, past and present, will be interested to hear that he has gone into the second-hand furniture business' – what a scoop that would be for next term's issue! But it is not my duty, I am thankful to say, to provide sensational items for my old school magazine. The whole thing is not worth a moment's thought.

Megrim came in about the Debating Society, and I asked him (quite casually, of course, and without giving anything away) if he happened to know anything about second-hand furniture in Wales.

'You ask the most extraordinary questions, Wentworth,' he said. 'I imagine it is like second-hand furniture anywhere else. Huge wall mirrors and purplish bureaux with dangling brass handles. Why?'

'Oh, nothing,' I said. 'It doesn't matter.' I then tried to change the subject, but Megrim is one of those people who worry at a casual conversation like a dog with a bone.

'Suppose I were to ask you whether you knew anything about ironmongery in Northumberland,' he said. 'Wouldn't that seem to you a bit odd? Or no, as a matter of fact I suppose it wouldn't. *Do* you know anything about ironmongery in Northumberland, Wentworth?'

I told him, as far as I remember, that I knew nothing about ironmongery, or about Northumberland either for that matter. I said, quite politely, that I was not in the least interested in ironmongery and that, if everything was now settled about the Debate, I had some rather important letters to write. But you might as well give a hint to a rhinoceros.

'*I'm* not interested in second-hand furniture,' he said, with a look round my room which I very much resented, 'unless it's good, that is. But I *am* interested, naturally, in why you should be interested. In South Wales of all places. Of course, if it's a secret – '

'There is nothing secret about it,' I interrupted, well knowing what would happen in a place like this if anybody thought there was. 'It simply happens – a friend of mine was asking me about it. I am only sorry I bothered you with the thing.' I do not care for prevarication, but with a certain type of persistent bore one sometimes has no alternative.

'I see,' he said. 'I tell you what though. You know Roberts, up the lane?'

'Well?' I said.

'Well, I've got an idea he, or it may have been his sister, used to be in Antiques or something more or less in those parts. He might be able to help. I'll send the old boy along to you, shall I?'

'It is very kind of you,' I began, 'but – '

'No trouble,' he said in that off-hand way of his. 'I'm going that way in any case.' And he took himself off before I had a chance to tell him for goodness' sake to mind his own business. If only I knew of an ironmonger from Westmorland or some such place to plague Megrim with I could soon put a stop to this nonsense.

Roberts came to the back door after tea to tell me he had something in the handcart outside I might care to look at. I can't say I was greatly surprised, for these people always seem to get hold of the wrong end of the stick. Rather than involve myself in a long explanation to the effect that I was not interested in buying furniture but in the second-hand furniture business (which I certainly am *not*), I accompanied Roberts to the gate in no very good temper.

'That's a Swansea piece, that is,' he said. 'As you'll likely know.'

It was a small chest of drawers, hardly fit even for a boy's dormitory, and quite useless to me. However, I offered the man half a crown to be rid of him. It did not seem fair that he should have had his journey for nothing, under a misapprehension that was probably not altogether his fault. But he was by no means grateful. He said it was a genuine antique. 'Why, it's worth more than that as firewood,' he told me.

'I dare say,' I said. 'But there's the labour of chopping it up.'

In the end, feeling a little ashamed of having allowed ill temper to rule my tongue, I gave him ten shillings for it, which

I can ill afford, and asked him to put the chest in the tool-shed. It seems a poor return, so far, for my advertisement in *The Times*.

Perhaps tomorrow's post will bring me something a little more promising.

# A Missed Opportunity

It is all very well to say that all experience is an arch, as
Tennyson somewhere or other claims, wherethro' gleams that
untravelled world and so on and so forth. I used often to recite
the passage, I remember, in my younger days when things went
a little awry – to myself, that is: one does not declaim poetry
aloud up and down the corridors of a first-class preparatory
school! – and was much comforted by it at times. We live and
learn, I suppose, would be another way of saying the same
thing. But I very much doubt whether Alfred Tennyson, with
all respect to his memory, ever had such a day as I have had,
with nothing to show for it but a torn trouser-leg and a pocket
full of unwanted oats. All experience indeed! A hundred and
fifty miles all told, and an umbrella riddled with small shot
through no fault of my own, at the end of it. What kind of
untravelled world gleams through *that* particular arch, one is
tempted to ask.

Whatever it may be, I feel disinclined this evening, with
what I fear may be a heavy cold coming on, to explore it. One
begins very seriously to doubt whether the insertion of my
advertisement in *The Times*, asking for short-term work in
positions of trust, etc., was altogether wise. Quite apart from
being pestered with second-hand furniture down here in Fenport, some of the offers of employment made to me through
the post have been ridiculous. One does not become a Bachelor
of Arts, I should hope, in order to exercise dogs from 2.30 to
4.0 p.m. every afternoon except Thursdays. Nor am I the man,
as those who know me best will agree, to recommend hosiery

to total strangers on a commission basis! There are times when I really think the world has gone mad.

Still, to be fair, as I always try to be, the post in search of which I set off to Wiltshire early this morning appeared to be very much more in my line of country and might indeed have suited me well, but for a chain of ill-luck such as I have rarely experienced. An opening as companion-secretary to a gentleman temporarily incapacitated by an accident while hunting is the kind of thing I am looking for, at twelve guineas a week with board and keep and travelling expenses refunded after the interview if unsuccessful. I had little doubt in my mind, as I walked to the station to catch the 8.45 local to Southampton, that provided this Colonel Ripley proved to be of a congenial cast of mind we should very soon come to terms. Nor have I any reason to doubt *now* that we should have done so, had I been permitted to meet the gentleman.

Little is to be gained by jotting down the details of this vexatious business. The milk has been spilt, in every sense of the phrase, and there is an end of it. But I owe it to myself to point out that had adequate transport been available at Stenshall nothing of the kind would have arisen. I was thunderstruck when a rather dull-witted porter there told me that no buses ran past the Manor House on Wednesdays. 'There was a car come to meet the 11.48 down from Blandford,' the man said. 'But I doubt it could have been for you, seeing you just got off the 12.6 up from Temple Combe. Not that Mrs Ripley didn't go back empty in a bit of a taking, at that.'

There seemed no point in explaining to the fellow that I had been badly advised by a ticket-inspector at Bournemouth West, so I simply asked him what I had better do. After some thought he told me in his slow country way that Grimley's van would be coming 'up street' in a minute or two and might be able to drop me 'there or thereabouts', as he was pleased to put it. Having no alternative I agreed to this curious approach to my future employer, and very soon found myself jolting along in a bucket seat beside a civil young man, who seemed genuinely sorry that he had not the time to take me round past the Manor gates. He was going 'sort of more along the back of

their place, like', he told me (How strangely these people talk!)
but would drop me at the nearest point, where I could cut
across a couple of fields and up through the farm. 'Ten
minutes,' he said, 'at the outside', and late though I was it
seemed the best thing to do. One cannot pick and choose,
really, when nothing else offers.

I could not foresee, of course, that a heavy downpour of rain
would catch me out in the open as soon as I had entered the
second of the two fields indicated to me. Naturally I had my
umbrella with me, but I most certainly did not wish to appear
for my interview with sodden trouser legs and I therefore
turned left-handed and made all possible haste along the
hedgerow to a barn or shed which stood in the near corner of
the field, intending to shelter there through the worst of it. It
was here that I had my first stroke of misfortune. The building
was very dark inside, and though I could just make out that it
contained some kind of machinery I had no warning that there
was need to exercise more than my usual caution until I happened, while shaking my umbrella, to engage the crook of it
with what must I suppose have been a lever or handle. I gave
no more than a slight tug, to free it, and at once noticed a
whirring and clanking noise suggesting that some sort of
mechanical operation had been set in motion. Then a considerable quantity of oats, a very considerable quantity, was
precipitated over my head and shoulders from above.

This incident, though momentarily startling and confusing
in the indifferent light, was not in itself, to one who is accustomed to life's ups and downs, more than a passing inconvenience, and I should not have mentioned the mishap had
not its immediate consequences proved so vexatious. Oats are
less easy to brush off the clothing than some other kinds of
cereal, and though I did my best in the few minutes that
elapsed before the rain stopped I suppose it was inevitable that
I should leave what amounted to be a trail behind me on
resuming my walk. Be that as it may, I soon became aware that
I was being followed by several farmyard fowls, which
appeared from nowhere after the manner of these creatures.
Their number and speed increased rapidly, to my dismay, so

that by the time I had reached the farther hedge, beyond which the roofs and chimneys of what must be Manor Farm were clearly visible, they had become a serious embarrassment. I am not easily put out, but no one cares to arrive for an appointment attended by a flock of gaping poultry. I therefore made an attempt to drive them off with gestures of my umbrella, which I still think was the only sensible course in the circumstances. There was an outburst of cackling and one or two fowls rose into the air with the usual exaggerated loss of feathers, and I was preparing to take advantage of the diversion to slip through a gateway when I heard the sound of running feet and a man's voice from beyond the hedgerow shouting, 'Get over left there, quick!'

Not knowing to whom he was speaking I checked the swing I was taking at a particularly pertinacious hen (a White Wyandotte, I think) and unluckily lost my grasp on my umbrella, which flew into the hedge some distance to my right, where it lodged quivering. At once there was a further cry of 'There he goes!' followed by the roar of firearms, and I found myself temporarily blinded by a mêlée of excited hens.

'Hi!' I called out. 'I say there!'

'What the devil are *you* doing?' a rough voice replied, and looking up I saw a tallish man in gaiters at the gateway, with a younger fellow (looking pretty scared, I thought) behind him.

'I might well ask you that,' I answered, getting to my feet in no very good temper. 'Is it your custom in this part of the country to shoot at visitors without warning?'

'There was a fox,' the younger fellow said sheepishly. 'In the hedge yonder. They get after the fowls, see?'

'Fox, indeed!' I said, and without another word I strolled across and retrieved my umbrella, which, to my great mortification, I found to be shot through and through.

'You tailored un good and proper, Fred,' the tall man said with a laugh.

'Somebody will have to pay for this,' I remarked sternly. 'It is a most outrageous thing.'

'You was trespassing,' the man said. 'Creeping about the hedges. Who are you, and what do you want?'

'See them birds pecking at his turn-ups?' the young hobble-dehoy put in. 'He's mostly chock-a-block with grain, or something of that, if you ask me.'

'So that's the game, eh?' the other man said.

'My name is Wentworth,' I told them, sick and tired of this meaningless folly. 'I have an urgent appointment with Colonel Ripley. Be so good as to direct me to the Manor House at once, please.'

My manner must have made it clear to them with whom they had to deal. But even so I was obliged to show these two fools my letter from the Colonel before they would permit me to pass. 'Best call in at the farmhouse and see Mrs Jellaby,' the elder said finally, perhaps in a belated attempt to make amends. 'She'll maybe run you up in the Land Rover.'

One would have thought that I had had enough trouble and delay already, and might now hope that the final stages of this tiresome journey would be comparatively plain sailing. But I have often found that if ill-luck dogs one at the start of a day it is difficult to shake it off completely before evening. One thing leads to another, as they say. Had I not been opening and shutting my umbrella as I descended the steepish track into the farmyard (in order, of course, to see whether the ribbing had been as irretrievably ruined as the fabric), I dare say I should not have been attacked, or at least menaced, by what at first glance I took to be a bull. With the quick instinct of a country-man I made a sideways leap on to a kind of trestle or stand for milk churns that chanced to be at the side of the track, not knowing of course that it was in fact a wheeled trailer – still less that my weight would raise the shaft, or towing-bar, from the ground and set the contraption in motion.

Heigh-ho! It's a weary world at times. Tennyson and his precious arch keep recurring to my mind as I sit by my gas fire and ponder on the tricks that fate can play. To the Greeks, of course, it was overweening pride that led to man's misfortunes, but nobody, I imagine, will accuse me of that. Still, one must not make too much of what was, after all, no more than a gentle spill. Had the trailer overturned in the steeper part of the track there might have been a nasty accident, but luckily it kept going until we were fairly down on the more level midden, when the towing-bar met some obstruction and I was catapulted on to a heap of – well, straw, and so on. Two churns, one of which at least seemed to be practically empty, had already fallen off, and I suppose it was the considerable clatter they made as they rolled away into a cart-shed that brought a rather heavily-built woman in slippers to the farmhouse door.

'What's the idea of this, then?' she asked.

I was anxious, as may be imagined, to give a full explanation of my unceremonious arrival, but whether it was the partial wetting I had had while running for shelter earlier on, or whether it was some effect of grain dust, akin to hay-fever, I was seized by a most uncharacteristic fit of sneezing, and for some little time remained sitting where I had fallen unable to say a coherent word.

'Such a racket!' the woman said. 'I'd have thought it was the Last Trump, if there'd been lightning with it.'

'Atishoo!' I said.

'I don't know, I'm sure,' she said, coming nearer. 'Look at your trousers!'

'Atchoo – atchoo – a-*tisho*!'

'Have you come far,' the woman asked curiously, 'just to give that carry-on?'

I continued to sneeze for some time, while the woman made no offer to help, contenting herself with a series of wondering exclamations and the absurd observation that it never rains but it pours. But at last the paroxysm began to abate and I was able to speak, though not at first freely.

'My name,' I said, struggling to my feet, 'is Woo – dear me – my name is *Atcher* . . .'

'Is that your umbrella and all?' the woman asked.

I think it was the state to which my faithful old brolly (a present from my colleagues, as a matter of fact, on my fiftieth birthday) – it was the sad condition of my old friend, when I recovered it from beneath the trailer, that made it clear to me that I must abandon any idea of calling upon Colonel Ripley, for that day at least. I decided to cut my losses, and take myself off with the least possible delay. I had had about enough, to tell the truth.

'Perhaps you will be good enough to give a message to Colonel Ripley?' I began briskly. 'As you can see – '

'How you ever come to be on that trailer,' the woman said. ' "Wagon Train" isn't in it.'

'Never mind that now,' I said. 'Please tell your master that Mr Wentworth was unable to keep his appointment today, owing to a combination of – a – , a – , – Confound it !'

'You'd better let it come,' she said.

' – owing to circumstances over which I had no control. Just tell him that, please. And that I – that Mr Woo – Woo – oh, devil take it, Woorasher! Say I shall be writing,' I shouted angrily. 'And good day to you.'

'I'll tell him you called,' the woman cried after me, and burst into peal after peal of totally unnecessary laughter. There has been a sorry decline in manners, I fear, even in the country-side.

So there it is. I suppose I should write some sort of explanation to Colonel Ripley, asking for another appointment, but I don't seem to have the heart for it, just now.

# A Comfortable Billet

It has turned out very well in the end, as is often the case if one keeps one's head and lets things take their course. Some men, I dare say, would have given up after the unlucky experience I had on my first attempt to keep an appointment at the Manor House, Stenshall, Wiltshire, but schoolmasters have to learn to take the rough with the smooth. A very courteous letter from Colonel Ripley, regretting any inconvenience to which I had been put and suggesting a date for a second visit, decided me to try again – and here, in short, I am, snugly housed in a bedroom twice the size of my little crib at Fenport, and nothing in the way of draughts to speak of considering the age of the house.

Needless to say, my second journey down here went off without a hitch. Mrs Ripley drove me from the station, pointing out this and that as we went along. She is a charming lady, and we very soon found out that she was at school with a Miss Soulby whose nephew was at Burgrove during my time there, though we could neither of us remember the boy's name. A strange coincidence, which helped, I think. She is the kind of person with whom one at once feels at ease.

So, in his rather more boisterous way, is the Colonel. He has broken a leg, poor fellow, and is obliged to spend the day on a couch in his study, but looks very fit and healthy none the less. I naturally attempted an apology for my failure to get farther than Manor Farm on the Wednesday, but he brushed it aside with great good humour.

'Never laughed so much in my life, when I heard,' he said, slapping his good knee. 'Hens flying all over the place, shouting and shots in the five-acre, and then down the hill you come like a bat out of hell, balancing on a two-wheeled trailer by God, if Mrs Jellaby is to be believed, with oats pouring out of your ears and milk scattering this way and that like a Goddess of Plenty in her chariot – if I could have been *there* dammit ! – and then *blam* ! head-first into a heap of dung and a hundred and fifty-six sneezes to round it off. What an entry ! "Mary," I said to my wife – didn't I, Mary ? – "we must see this joker, if it's the last thing we do," I said, "and get the real inside story." Well, you know how it is. Mrs Jellaby seems to think you did it on purpose.'

'I dare say Mr Wentworth didn't find the experience very funny at the time, dear,' Mrs Ripley said in her gentle way, while I was considering how best to take this very exaggerated account of an admittedly absurd contretemps.

'It was certainly an unconventional way to arrive,' I said at last with a smile. 'But these things happen.' And I gave them a short account of what really occurred, to which I must say they both listened with a great deal of appreciation. But then I have always had the knack of telling a story, even if it is, up to a point, against myself.

'Lucky you didn't hurt yourself, my boy,' Colonel Ripley said, when he had had his laugh out. 'You must bill me for those trousers – and the umbrella, of course. We might have it mounted and hung up in the hall with the stags' heads and other trophies. What is it, by the way – an eight-pointer?'

I could not help joining in the laughter at this ridiculous notion, and capped the Colonel's fancy by suggesting that perhaps a plaster cast could be made of my ruined trousers. This sally had even Colonel Ripley beaten, and after a little silence he said that perhaps he ought to come to the point and explain what kind of help he was looking for during his enforced idleness. It would be mainly answering the telephone, I gathered, and seeing to this and that, as his wife had to be out in the car, on farming and village matters, a great deal of the time. I replied that I should be happy to make myself useful in any way that was within my powers, and after some further conversation about detail, the thing was settled. They gave me a satisfying lunch of steak-and-kidney-pudding, which I always enjoy, and I left, promising to return with my baggage on the Monday. 'Let us know if you think of taking the short cut across the fields,' the Colonel called after me, but not being able to think of a suitable reply, I contented myself with a wave of the hand. The joke, in any case, is beginning to wear a bit thin.

So here, as I say, I am, safely back again at the Manor, with two very full and interesting days' work behind me. The Colonel has wide interests and keeps me busy on errands of one kind and another. Some of them might be thought a bit, well, *infra dig* for a man in my position, but I am no believer in making a fuss, especially as Colonel Ripley always remembers to preface an unusual request with the words 'Be a good chap,' which keeps things on a proper footing. Or so it seems to me.

It is a varied life. This morning, for instance, there was an order for linseed cake to be hastened, a note to take to old Mrs Coombes at the cottage, and a parcel to be got off. Then I had to ring Rogers at the Bull and tell him it was off ('Never mind what,' the Colonel said, in answer to my natural inquiry. 'He'll know'), give a message to the Rector about the Boys' Club and ask Mrs Jellaby how Phoebe was doing. 'Oh, and while you're in the village,' he went on, while I scribbled my instructions down on the pad I have bought myself (quite the secretary, eh?), 'you might look Mathers up and ask him about the insurance on Felicity. I want to be sure she is adequately covered. And get me a P.O. for 18s. 6d., will you? There's money in the drawer there. My wife has to be over at Sturminster all day in the car, I'm afraid, but there's an old bike of mine in the garage. It's got a basket, so bring a few leeks from the farm – only don't bring 'em to me, as you did with that fish yesterday, take 'em straight in to cook. There's a good chap,' he added, as my eyebrows rose.

There was also a message about a sack of potatoes that Mrs Ripley would deliver tomorrow, but I did not quite get the name of the person to whom I was to give it. Colonel Ripley gets rather impatient if one asks him to repeat things – it is his leg, I dare say, that makes him a little brusque at times – and

in any case there was no need to bother him. The message was
certainly to one of the people I had to call upon on other
matters, so I had only to keep asking as I went along. That is
what we used to call 'using your initiative' in the Army, where
one soon learns to find things out for oneself. Colonel Ripley
rather reminds me of my old C.O. in a way; he has a trick of
taking it for granted that one knows what he is talking about,
which of course is not always the case at first when the subject
is an unfamiliar one such as Army Council Instructions or, as
in this instance, livestock and so on. Had he made it clear to me
that Felicity was a mare, which I could hardly be expected to
know, my interview with Mrs Mathers (to take a case in point)
would certainly have gone off a great deal more smoothly.

When a rather slatternly woman came to the door of No. 7,
Cadnam Row, in answer to my knock, and told me that Mr
Mathers was out, I naturally assumed that I was speaking to
Mrs Mathers, as indeed I was. 'Was it something important?'
she asked me, and I thought there could be no harm in passing
on the gist of my message, particularly as I was under the
impression that it concerned her.

'It was only that Colonel Ripley wanted to know,' I began
' – the question is whether you are adequately covered.'

The woman flushed up and immediately glanced down at
her attire, and following the direction of her eyes I realized
that, in that sense, she certainly was not. To get over what
might have been a momentary awkwardness, I decided to
change the subject and, averting my eyes, asked her casually
whether she was expecting a sack of potatoes.

'It's no business of yours what I'm expecting, nor when,' she
cried furiously, and to my utter astonishment slammed the
door in my face, giving me no chance at all to explain, as I was
anxious to do in my own good time, that my opening question
referred simply to insurance. These country people take a deal
of understanding. It was a relief to move on to the Rectory,
where I had a pleasant chat with the incumbent, a man of
my own kidney with whom there was no need to fear mis-
understandings or embarrassments. He told me much about
Stenshall and its good people, which will be a help to me

as I go to and fro, and in return I explained that I was acting as companion-secretary to Colonel Ripley, while he was laid up. 'Though I'm more of a glorified errand boy than a secretary, it seems,' I added, smiling to show that I did not really take my employment amiss.

'Well, it's something to be glorified,' he responded. 'I only live in hopes of attaining that status!' And on that friendly note we parted.

My final call was upon Mrs Jellaby, down at the Manor Farm, an encounter which, to tell the truth, I put off as long as I could.

'Well I never!' she cried, throwing up her hands in mock astonishment. 'If it isn't Mr Woo-Woo-Woorasher!'

I had half expected something of the kind, after my previous meeting with the lady, and deliberately ignored the impertinence. 'My name is Wentworth,' I said quietly. 'Am I right in thinking I am addressing Mrs Jellaby?'

'I can't forget it – ever,' she said. 'I was in the front, not to tell a lie, when the clatter starts up, and I said to myself "It's the atomic!" I said, "Or if it's not that," I said – '

'Mrs Jellaby! I have been asked by my employer, Colonel Ripley – '

'And sneeze!' the woman went on, wiping her eyes. 'Sitting there in the muck, kind of baffled, and not a word out of you but A-ratchoo till I thought to myself – '

'Mrs Jellaby!'

'But there! Come in do, Mr Wentworth,' Mrs Jellaby said, pulling herself together at last. 'I'm forgetting my manners. A glass of cider won't do either of us any harm.'

I was somewhat loth, as may be imagined, to accept hospitality after what had passed, but I had my mission to fulfil and took three glasses before I could get to the point. I must say that Mrs Jellaby proved, on better acquaintance, to be a very amiable woman and quite devoted to Mrs Ripley, as who is not? She is inclined to be a little voluble, perhaps, and utterly unable, like all these farming folk, to appreciate that what is clear to her may not be equally clear to an outsider.

'Phoebe?' she said at last, in answer to my repeated

inquiries. 'We're not happy about her at all, not really. She's still not letting it down, tell the Colonel.'

'Dear me!' I said. 'Yes. I see. Not letting what down exactly, Mrs Jellaby?'

'Why, her milk,' Mrs Jellaby said, staring at me as though I were out of my mind. 'Whatever else, Mr Wentworth?'

'Of course, of course,' I said. 'I hadn't realized – that is to say, what precisely do you think is the cause of this – of the failure? Just in case the Colonel wants to know, you know.'

'They say I'm an out-of-date old silly, Mr Wentworth,' Mrs Jellaby replied, leaning forward very earnestly with her hands on her knees, 'but it's *my* opinion she's got a cold in her bag.'

'I see,' I said, wondering what some of my old colleagues would have thought of this extraordinary conversation. 'Yes. No doubt. One can only hope, in that case, that, unlike another lady I could name, she is adequately covered!'

I had her there! It was *her* turn not to understand what *I* was talking about.

# A Cricket Dinner

'Where's that ass, Wentworth?'

I could hardly believe my ears when I heard my employer refer to me in this offensive way, and I dare say he could tell by my manner, as with a quiet 'I am here, Colonel Ripley,' I stepped into the study and stood waiting with my pad at the ready, that I was not accustomed to such treatment.

'Oh, there you are!' he said lightly. 'You mustn't mind me, Wentworth. Mary will tell you I call all my friends asses.'

If he expected to mollify me by the insinuation that I was now more of a friend than an employee he only partially succeeded.

'That may be. They are in a position to return the compliment,' I said warmly. 'I, unfortunately, am not.'

'You manage to make your point very nicely, all the same,' he replied with a good-natured grin, and feeling that honours were even I let the matter drop, particularly as Mrs Ripley gave me a conspiratorial wink, as much as to say 'You put him in his place very adroitly there, Mr Wentworth.'

'What's this I hear about your asking Mrs Mathers if she was expecting a sack of potatoes, you old rascal,' the Colonel went on, bursting into a roar of laughter. 'If *you*'d had eight children in nine years, and another on the way, I dare say – '

'Good heavens!' I cried, flushing to the roots of my hair. 'So that was why – I had no idea.'

'It's all over the village,' Mrs Ripley said. 'And nobody enjoyed the story more than old Mathers.'

The subject hardly seemed a suitable one for mixed company, I must say. However, it was not I that had brought it up.

'What an unlucky thing!' I said, really distressed. 'I shall certainly do my best to explain and apologize, to Mrs Mathers.'

But to my surprise they both opposed this plan. 'You'd have to choose your words pretty carefully,' the Colonel pointed out; and with this, on reflection, I agreed.

It is difficult to avoid putting one's foot in it occasionally in these unfamiliar surroundings. Still, I am picking things up very quickly as I go along and in another week or so ought to be thoroughly *au fait* with farming affairs. By then, of course, my visit will be drawing to an end. The Colonel's leg is mending rapidly – 'I have you to thank for that, Wentworth,' he told me the other day. 'You are the best spur to recovery an invalid ever had' (a compliment that I greatly appreciated, as he is by no means over-ready with praise) – and as soon as he can get about my usefulness here will be over. I shall be sorry to go, in many ways, for they are friendly people hereabouts and I think I may claim to have made quite a hit with them. Everybody seems to know who one is, and so on, in a remarkably short space of time and to be anxious to stop for a chat. Only yesterday a total stranger hailed me to inquire whether my hay-fever was better, which I am sure was well meant, though I am not as it happens a sufferer.

As a matter of fact, it may well be convenient for me to leave in the fairly near future. Other things apart, I have had a belated reply to my advertisement in *The Times* from a Mr Bennett, of London, inquiring whether I might be free to accompany his two boys to Switzerland in about a fortnight's time. *In loco parentis*, I gather. One does not get away to the Continent very often on a pension like mine, and it seems too good an opportunity to miss, all being well. Still, all that is in the future. For the moment, there are things to be seen to in the outhouses! Upon my word, I sometimes wonder what the world is coming to. 'Be a good chap and nip out to the loft over the stables,' the Colonel began, so I knew there was something rather menial in the wind. How the boys at Burgrove would smile if they could see their old master checking over apples in a granary and putting the affected ones in a

basket to take to Mrs Jellaby later – though what the good
woman wants with rotten apples is more than I can say.

Tonight, apparently, I am to represent Colonel Ripley at
the Annual Dinner of the Stenshall Cricket Club, of which he
is President, so that one cannot complain of a lack of variety
here. If it isn't one thing it's another, I said to Mrs Ripley in
an unguarded moment, and she agreed. Her sympathy and
understanding mean a great deal to me at times. She would
have made an ideal headmaster's wife, had things turned out
differently all round, with just the right manner towards
parents, and it grieves me to see her carrying pig-meal about
in an old pair of breeches. That is clumsily put, but the sentiment is sincere. 'Let *me*, Mrs Ripley,' I said to her on one
occasion, and rather than hurt my feelings by refusing she
handed over the bucket and thanked me very nicely. I think
the unexpected attention touched her quite deeply, which
explains why she went away without remembering to tell me
where to take the pig-meal. There are no pigs here, as far as I
know, so I had to get rid of it as best I could. The point is that
her husband rather takes her for granted, in my opinion – not
that it is any business of mine, of course.

Cricket holds the Empire together I told them, as one good
fellow to another, and they liked it. Everybody sang afterwards, though I had had no warning, mind, not a word till it
was too late and off I had to go. The Colonel knew. Ripley
must have known what I had to do and I did it, no thanks to
him. He never said. Anybody ought to, when people have to
speak, but there it was.

'I am speaking on the President's behoof,' I said, which was
true, despite the fact that I didn't know until I was told. What
I mean is nobody told me before. 'Call upon Mr Wentworth to
propose toast,' some fellow said, and there I was. I wouldn't
have nine times out of ten. I said that, too, making no bones
about it to clear the air. Nine times out of ten I wouldn't, I told
them, but this is the tenth. 'Have some more cider,' they said,
but I refused, unless that was later. I never drink more when
I have to speak. Actually it was later I dare say because I

didn't know I was going to before, as it turned out. I am
scribbling on my bed while I remember, in case I forget what
I was going to say. The Rector spoke, I remember that, and I
spoke and another man spoke about a whip-round for bats ('In
the belfry?' I said to my neighbour, but had to nudge him and
repeat it, by which time the man – not this man, the other –
was thanking the wives for helping with tea, so the point was
lost). Where was I? For two pins I would go to bed, but my
pyjama top is missing. Play the game I told them and everybody cheered. 'Stand up the man who shot my umbrella!' I
said, mixing *seria cum joco*, and they cheered again. Nobody
stood up so I sat down, having no more to say at present. It is
a rule I always follow when speaking, but they all shouted, 'Go
on, go on!' and somebody said, 'You have forgotten the toast,
sir.'

'What toast is that?' I asked, not having been told properly
before, and the Rector said it was the Club, which was a great
honour for one who had so newly come among them. Not the
Rector, naturally. I mean it was a great honour for me, or so
I told them. 'I am only the Colonel's legate, of course,' I said
– meaning to add 'his *broken* legate' for fun, but a bald-
headed man got in first with the quip, and in the general
laughter I could not think where in the world my pyjama coat
can have got to. So I sat down again. Then the Rector proposed the toast of the Stenshall Cricket Club, and I made a
short reply, which I forget. A Mr Binns told me I was the hit
of the evening, but I ought to have been told before, in my
opinion. Still, we all enjoyed myself and sang songs, which is
the great thing.

It was under my shirt, of all places.

The days speed pleasantly by, with little of note to record.
Colonel Ripley is up and hobbling about now, I am glad to say.
Much of his old tetchiness has gone, too, which makes him
easier to work with. Had he stepped into that puddle of pig-
meal while he was still confined to his couch – not that he
could have done so, naturally; I am merely drawing a com-
parison – he would have made a great deal more fuss about

it, or I'm a Dutchman. Actually, it was a kind of mash for chickens, which I should have disposed of elsewhere had I known that my employer would be poking about in the shrubbery for some unexplained reason.

'Don't tell me *why* you put it there, Wentworth,' he said, before I had so much as hinted that I had anything to do with the matter. 'Some other time, perhaps, when I've an hour or two to spare. We must just be thankful you didn't send it to the Church Bazaar, along with that load of manure.' He was smiling as he spoke, or I should certainly have resented this unnecessary allusion to a perfectly understandable mistake. If the Colonel has a fault, as he undoubtedly has, it is a tendency to harp on trivialities that are over and done with. In any case I am no stenographer, and errors are bound to occur occasionally when instructions are rattled off faster than I can write. It was on the tip of my tongue to tell him that it was no part of a companion-secretary's duties to dispatch manure, to the Church Bazaar or anywhere else.

'Did I ever hear, by the way,' he went on, 'where my old hats went to?'

They went to Lady Wimbury at the Grange, as he very well knew, and as soon as she returned them with a short note I realized that there had been a muddle and took immediate steps to put things right. No harm whatever was done, as far as I can see, except for a little staining outside the village hall, which will wash off. It would have been different if the load had been delivered *inside*.

'It would, yes,' Colonel Ripley agreed, when I pointed this out. 'Now, be a good chap and give Mrs Ripley a hand in the stables, will you?'

Be a good chap, indeed! Be a good ostler and general factotum would be a likelier way of putting it.

Still, there are many compensations. I happened to be enjoying the sunshine on the terrace after luncheon when two or three shots rang out down by the farm. The men are rabbiting, I expect.

'Hullo!' I heard the Colonel remark, through his open study window. 'They're after Wentworth again!'

'Oh, I *hope* not,' Mrs Ripley replied, with her pleasant laugh. 'He's such a dear, really.'

'I wouldn't have missed him for worlds,' the Colonel said.

I moved away then, of course, being no eavesdropper. But I had heard enough. The sun went in after a minute or two, but I scarcely noticed it. There are things more warming than sunshine.

# In Foreign Parts

The snow-capped peaks tower upwards and the lake shimmers in the bright sunlight. Had I the pen of a Ruskin I dare say I could describe the scene with more vividness, though of course there is less need for that kind of thing now that so many people travel abroad. After all, when one has seen a thing for oneself one does not much want to hear what somebody else thought about it – a point that modern writers often forget. One has one's snapshots, and so on, if memory proves treacherous, whereas in Ruskin's time I suppose even picture postcards were something of a rarity.

Still, it is certainly very pretty here on Lake Lucerne – or Vierwaldstattersee, as it is rather cumbrously called on the map (*Touristenkarte*!) provided free by the hotel – and I cannot help congratulating myself on my wisdom in advertising for temporary employment in *The Times*. There goes the steamer for Vitznau, a typically foreign contraption, absurdly broad in the beam for such calm waters, though it all adds to the fun in a way. We shall be aboard her in a day or two, I expect, when the boys have had a proper rest after the long journey. 'Take them about a bit and show them things,' Mr Bennett said to me at our last interview, and I feel sure that a trip round the lake would be in accordance with his wishes. Lucerne itself we must certainly see. Then there is the ascent of the Rigi, whence the views, so the hall porter tells me, are very fine. It will be best, I think, to draw up some kind of programme after lunch.

We have already been up one mountain, as a matter of fact, rather unexpectedly. Up to a point, that is. A man of my experience does not take a couple of boys all the way up a mountain by accident, I need hardly say. What happened was that on our way by train to Brunnen, where we are staying, from Zurich whither we had flown by the night plane, I distinctly heard a woman say that this was a Schnellzug (she was speaking in German, of course) and did not stop at Brunnen. As the train was then standing at Schwyz, which I luckily – or perhaps unluckily, as it turned out – knew to be the last stop before Brunnen, the last *station* that is to say, I bundled the boys out with our luggage in double-quick time, only to find from a most helpful official that the train which had now left did in fact stop at Brunnen and that the next one on would leave in an hour and a half. This was rather a facer, as we had not yet breakfasted, but the official suggested that we take a tram instead, from just outside the station, which we very soon did. I thought it best not to explain our little slip-up to the boys, as William was getting fretful and even his elder brother Geoffrey looked rather pale. Boys are happier, especially far from home, when they feel that everything is going smoothly, and a little harmless deception is often justified, in their own interests.

It was for this reason that, when the tram after a short run reached the centre of Schwyz and everyone alighted, I concealed my annoyance at having been misdirected and, with a cheerful 'Only one more change now,' simply got out and followed the rest into a waiting bus. Soon we were bowling along a delightful valley and though, had I been in my own country and a little less tired, I suppose I should have made more careful inquiries, I had no hint of trouble until a conductor came along flourishing his clippers and I demanded 'Drei nach Brunnen', with a wave of my hand at the two boys. The conductor shook his head and said 'Stoos', of which I could make neither head nor tail, so I simply handed him some money which unfortunately turned out to be Italian. How it came to be in my right-hand trouser pocket I cannot think. It is my custom when travelling abroad to make a very careful distribution of money, documents and other valuables, to ensure that each is handy as and when required. Thus on the present occasion I had our passports safely in my inside breast pocket with the return air tickets pinned to the inner back cover. Travellers' cheques, as always, were in my left-hand hip pocket, which buttons, Swiss notes in my outside breast pocket secured with a safety-pin, and so on. Any English change I tie up in a handkerchief as soon as the frontier is crossed and keep for the time being in my left-hand trouser pocket. The small amount of Italian money I had brought with me in case we were able to make an excursion through the St Gotthard tunnel should have been in my top right-hand waistcoat pocket, and I got the shock of my life when in trying to explain all this to the conductor (with the aid of gestures, for he seemed a slow-witted sort of man) I put my fingers into the pocket in question and pulled out our return train tickets to Zurich! These should by rights have been in the front fob pocket of my trousers, but I soon gave up the attempt to make this point clear to the conductor, for after a brief glance at them he became so verbose and unintelligible that I had difficulty in keeping calm. Geoffrey began to ask what was the matter, and to gain time I blew my nose without proper forethought and instantly scattered a considerable quantity of small change about the bus.

Everybody was most helpful in hunting about under the seats, etc., for the coins, which to my astonishment proved to be Swiss.

'Then where is my English money?' I cried involuntarily as soon as I saw that the money they were handing to me was in francs. This started a fresh search among a number of the passengers who seemed to understand English, until I asked them not to trouble. 'It will turn up, no doubt,' I said. 'I must have put it somewhere else.'

'Perhaps it's up the other nostril,' I heard young William say in a whisper to his brother, but I was unable to reprimand him at once for the impertinence as an English lady just in front of me was asking whether she could be of any help.

'I thought I heard you asking for Brunnen,' she said. 'This bus goes to Schattli, for the cable railway up to Stoos, you know.'

'I see,' I said. 'Yes. And from there to Brunnen?'

'Well, you have to come back again to Schwyz, of course, and then there's a tram. But you might as well come right up to Stoos while you are about it. It's lovely up there.'

So that is what we did. The boys seemed to think it was rather a long way round to Brunnen, but they enjoyed the cable railway and became much more lively when we found breakfast being served in a fine hotel up on the top. The lady, a Mrs Fitch who is staying at Brunnen apparently, was very kind, drawing our attention to Lake Lucerne away below to our left and pointing out a number of the surrounding heights. She is a most friendly person, in the prime of life, and seemed to be as relieved as I was when I finally found my English small change while taking my tobacco pouch from my right-hand hip-pocket. 'You shower money from *every* quarter, Mr Wentworth,' she said gaily.

All that, however, is by the way. Here we are safely in our hotel, with the boys resting in their room on my instructions and I myself lazily watching the steamer grow smaller in the distance. It was a fortunate chance that Mr Bennett noticed my advertisement, and fortunate for me too that he had found himself unable, at the last moment, to accompany his two sons on their holiday abroad and so was obliged to look about for a trustworthy companion and squire for the lads. We very soon came to terms, and I must say that he has been most generous in his provision for the jaunt. It is quite a new experience for me to have another man's money in my pockets to spend (which reminds me that I really must get my small change and so on re-sorted and properly disposed or goodness knows what I shall be finding in my waistcoat next. Piastres, eh? Or a return ticket to Baker Street!). But I dare say I shall quickly get used to it.

Of course, it is a responsibility. But then, as I told Mr Bennett when he asked me whether I was used to taking charge – this was at our first meeting, to be fair, before he had had a chance to sum me up – I have taken parties of up to a dozen boys abroad in my time and not a broken leg between them. He looked a little dubious at this recommendation for a moment, but his brow cleared when I explained that I was referring to winter sports holidays. 'I see,' he said. 'Yes. I was not thinking of any physical danger so much. Geoffrey is a steady, sensible boy as a rule, but William – the younger boy, you know – is apt to run a little wild at times. I suppose you – '

'Oh, that!' I said, laughing. 'You must set your mind at rest on *that* score.' It was really too funny to think that I might be alarmed at the prospect of keeping two youngsters of eleven and thirteen in order. 'Why I have had fifteen of them at me at once before now,' I began, recollecting an occasion at Burgrove when the electric light failed – but, realizing that he was probably too busy a man to want to listen to stories of an assistant master's early days, I left it at that. In any case, by the day after tomorrow at latest he should have my postcard announcing our arrival after an uneventful journey, and his mind will be at rest.

News of our little diversion up the Stooshorn has somehow got round the hotel, and there has been some flattering comment on our energy in tackling a mountain before breakfast on our way out from England. 'Been up the Rigi yet, Mr Wentworth?' somebody called out as we made our way in to lunch, and a party of young Dutchmen began to sing 'There'll always be an England', *sotto voce*. I took it in good part, as one should on a holiday, but when I pulled out my handkerchief during the second course and some total strangers pretended to hunt about under their table I thought the joke had gone far enough and spoke pretty sharply to young William for giggling. It is the first time he has heard the rough side of my tongue, and I think it surprised him.

It looks as though somebody has been making a story out of what was, after all, a very trivial mishap in the bus. I confess that I glanced momentarily at Mrs Fitch (who sits alone, I notice), but meeting her wide-eyed and friendly smile dismissed the thought as unworthy.

# A Trip up the Rigi

I put on my pullover this morning, feeling in holiday mood, though one misses the extra pockets afforded by a waistcoat, and asked the boys at breakfast how they would like to make an expedition to the top of the Rigi, which seems to be the thing to do here.

Geoffrey asked me how high it was, and I told him I believed it was well over five thousand feet.

'Isn't that rather potty?' William said. He is at the age when they make rather a point of not being impressed and has to be taken down a peg or two now and then, in a friendly way.

'You must be careful not to trip over it when you aren't looking, William,' I said. 'That is, if you are thinking of making this trivial excursion on foot. Geoffrey and I are too old to make light of five thousand feet and will be going up by train.'

'In a ship first,' Geoffrey said. 'In a jolly old *dampfschiff*. Will Mrs Fitch be coming with us, Herr Wentworth?'

I suppose it is natural for boys to giggle at foreign words, though my own view is that that sort of thing should be kept for occasions when no foreigners are about whose feelings may be hurt. I contented myself, for the moment, with a slight frown to show that I was not greatly amused (often the best way with over-excited boys) and merely asked why he imagined that Mrs Fitch would be joining us.

'Well, she seems to. She came up the Urmiberg, I mean – and that other place, when we went up by mistake.'

'The Urmiberg catches the worm,' William put in, and both boys laughed so immoderately at this senseless pun, if such it could be called, that I was forced to check them. 'People are

looking round,' I said, and led the way out of the breakfast
room (or *Speisesaal* in the local lingo), humming a little tune as
I sometimes do when a little put out. Not that William meant
to be impertinent, I think. Boys are apt to say the first thing
that comes into their heads, whether it means anything or not.

It was pure chance, really, that Mrs Fitch happened to be
at the hotel entrance yesterday afternoon as we were setting
out to walk to the cable-car that runs up to the Urmiberg from
the outskirts of Brunnen. Naturally she inquired where we
were going, and one thing led to another as it so often does. She
is very well acquainted with the district and has already promised to show us another little railway that starts quite near
the hotel and goes up to Morschach and Axenstein, whatever
they may be. If she had said Rosencrantz and Guildenstern it
would have been all the same to me. In any case, I see no harm
in it at my age. More was lost on Morschach's Fields, I fancy!
But I must not let the sunshine and heady air of Switzerland
betray me into young master William's habit of punning, however apt.

How astonishing, in passing, is the industry of the Swiss! It
seems that they cannot see a mountain peak without at once
putting a railway of some kind up it. Often, too, they build a
hotel at the top of it – which is natural enough, I suppose,
when one considers the number of visitors who make the
ascent. Unless, indeed, the hotel was there first, which would
certainly make the construction of the railway or funicular
more understandable. To take people up to the hotel, I mean.
But, in that case, it is hard to see how the materials and so on
were taken up to the hotel in the first place. It is like the chicken
and the egg, as I said to the hall-porter when discussing the
problem with him after breakfast; but he does not, I think,
understand English as well as he would have one believe. He
simply directed me to the *Speisesaal*, from which of course I
had only just come. I thanked him gravely, and to spare his
feelings pretended to glance over the letter rack until he went
away. One says 'thank you' for useless information a good
many times a day, I find, when abroad. It is all part of the
game.

We had a splendid day on the Rigi. The journey up the lake to Vitznau is most inspiring, with ever-changing views of the surrounding mountains and other points of interest, which I did my best to point out to my two charges. But they were generally on the other side of the boat, as boys so often are. So I chatted pleasantly with Mrs Fitch, who to my surprise turned out to be on board, and let my conscience go hang. After all, although it is my duty to see that this holiday is educational for them, in the fullest sense, it is no bad thing to let them broaden their minds on their own once in a way. I am always there, if they need me.

I had not realized, to tell the truth, that Mrs Fitch was a widow, until she told me that she had no one to care for now. I was wondering what to reply when the ship put in at Gersau, to pick up more passengers, and no sooner was this distraction over than Geoffrey came across to ask a question about my map, which he had very sensibly borrowed. So the opportunity was lost. However, as I had not been able to phrase any entirely suitable words of commiseration or consolation, no very great harm was done, I dare say. It is only that one likes not to be thought boorish or indifferent.

'The point is,' Geoffrey said, flattening the map on the seat beside me, 'this is supposed to be a lake, isn't it?'

'It is indeed,' I replied. 'With a maximum depth, just about where we are now I believe, of over 700 feet. So don't go leaning too far out over the rail, you two, or I shall be after you.'

'Then why is it called a "*See*"?' he demanded, stabbing his finger on the map. 'Look here, where it says Vierwaldstattersee. *See* means "sea", surely. It's swanking.'

'My dear boy,' I chuckled, after a quick look round to make sure that his remark had not been overheard, 'you really must not try to tell these good people what they should call their lakes. Switzerland has no sea coast, as you know, so why should they not use the word "sea" for such waters as they have? And very fine waters they are, too, are they not?' I concluded, raising my voice.

'They made a good job of it, anyway,' William joined in,

jabbing at the map as his brother had done. 'Look, it's the Vierwaldstattersee where we are now, and the Urner See where it goes round the corner at Brunnen . . .'

'*And* the Kussnachter See in that sort of creek thing,' Geoffrey said, 'and the Luzerner See or something there, and the Alpnacher See down here. Golly, it's a swizzle.'

'Five seas in one lake,' William counted. 'It's a good thing they haven't got a real sea or they'd soon run out of names.'

'And what is your definition of a real sea, young feller-me-lad?' I asked, to test him.

'Something that's salt anyway, and doesn't keep going round corners,' he declared, and we all burst out laughing.

'That would include Lot's wife, wouldn't it?' Mrs Fitch asked innocently.

'Or a bloater,' I added, to keep the fun going.

With one thing and another it was a light-hearted voyage, and so hot into the bargain that I had to go below before we reached Vitznau to remove my pullover. We had another good laugh as soon as we were ashore, when Geoffrey pointed out an English poster at the railway station saying 'Come to Skegness!' or some such place, and William wanted to know why on earth the Swiss should want to go *there*. 'Perhaps they like to look at a sea that doesn't go round corners,' I said with a twinkle, though I thought it right to add, when the laughter had died down, that young people must learn to admire the beauty of other countries without belittling their own. Mrs Fitch, for some reason, chose this moment to tell me that I was an unbelievable pet, a remark which I hope the boys did not overhear. They sometimes misunderstand grown-up teasing.

At Rigi Kaltbad, about two-thirds of the way to the actual summit, we left the train for luncheon, on Mrs Fitch's advice, and fed very comfortably on a terrace off some excellent veal steaks. We elders drank a bottle of lavaux (a local wine I am told) – an expense that I think Mr Bennett, my employer, would have approved, though I shall of course offer to reimburse him for Mrs Fitch's share of it. The strong air made me feel very fit. Looking out over the vista of mountains and down to the gleaming lake below it seemed a far cry from Dora's

Café in Fenport, where I sometimes have a cup of tea, and even from Burgrove School, happy though I have been there at times. A line or two of poetry, suming it all up, hovered at the back of my mind, but when I turned to share the thought with the others I found I could think of nothing but an oddly-worded notice about the boys' dirty laundry that was once put up on the School Board by a temporary matron. The mind works in curious ways at times.

And so to the summit, the Rigi Kulm itself. 'My goodness!' I could not help exclaiming, when the magnificent view burst upon us. 'What an amazing sight.' And everybody within ear-shot agreed with me. The boys simply stood and drank it all in, while I quietly spelt out the names of such peaks as I could identify from the map and reminded them how with the aid of trigonometry the height of each one of them could be accurately determined. Boys are always interested, in my not inconsiderable experience, to be told how the lessons they are learning at school are practically applied in the larger world outside, and I was bringing them up gradually from sea-level to a series of gradually established trig. points when the inevit-able tiresome bore, whom none of us knew from Adam, inter-vened with the announcement that on a really clear day it was possible to see the Flugelhorn, or it may have been the Grunt-stock.

'Indeed!' I said coldly. 'That must be delightful. But we can see all the peaks we need as it is, thank you.'

I fear I was a little abrupt, but really! He took himself off almost at once, but the spell was broken, and we too made for the train, to complete the round trip back to Brunnen, via Goldau and Schwyz. 'Well, well, well, well, well!' I said, smiling round at the others, as the train jogged and jolted its way down between rocky walls. 'We shall all be glad of a cup of tea when we get in.'

They were silent, however. It seemed odd that they should have nothing to say after what had been, when all is said and done, a remarkable experience.

# A Glimpse of Italy

It is no surprise, naturally, to find so many foreigners in Switzerland, but one had expected them to be Swiss. Or, to look at it from the Swiss point of view (as I make a point of trying to do when abroad – when in Switzerland, that is to say, and of course, *mutatis mutandis*, elsewhere) one had expected the foreigners to be *English*, which is what we are really, as I keep reminding the two boys, when we leave our own country. I mean it is we who are the foreigners, not the other way round, whereas in fact most of the others here seem to be Germans and Dutch and Danes and so on. Quite a cosmopolitan gathering, and very different from the old days when the English were the great travellers. Still, it all adds to the fun and has certainly opened the eyes of my two young charges. 'As you see, the English are not the only people in the world,' I sometimes say to them, to drive the lesson home.

To give them their due, both Geoffrey and William have been keen to make the very most of their continental holiday. 'When are we going to spend that Italian money?' they kept on asking me before we had been here a week, and in the end I agreed that we would make a little expedition through the St Gotthard tunnel into Italy. Just for the day, of course. I had had this plan in mind all along, as a matter of fact, and had the forethought to bring a few thousand lire with me, a fact of which the boys happened to be aware. But *having* money does not necessarily mean that one must *spend* it, as I felt it my duty to make clear to them. Besides, it does them no harm to be kept on tenterhooks for a while. Discipline is not always so easy to maintain while on holiday as at school; one can hardly set them impositions and so on, in cases of disobedience. But I had

only to say quietly, 'If you do that again I shall not take you
to Italy, William,' and that was the end of it for half an hour
or more. 'When you've a treat in store for the little devils,' as a
wise old colleague once said to me, 'keep it up your sleeve as
long as ever you can.'

I decided that Lugano would make a pleasant jaunt, and
we caught the ten-forty-three from Brunnen, arriving at our
destination after a thoroughly Alpine run at twenty-three
minutes past one. This gave us a good two hours in the place
before taking the half-past three train which gets back to
Brunnen at six-twenty-five, in good time for dinner. The boys
enjoyed the great tunnel, which I confess was a new experience
for me too, and eagerly pointed out to each other the Italian
names on the farther side. The sun seemed to shine with added
warmth as we ran down the southern slopes of the mighty
range and I think I dozed off for a while. At any rate the time
passed quickly, and we were all in high spirits and ready for
lunch as we left Lugano station and strolled to the lakeside in
search of a suitable place to eat.

'Look, *ristorante*!' cried Geoffrey. 'How super!'

Then William spotted the word *'impermeable'* in a shop
window full of raincoats, Geoffrey capped it with *'pantaloni'*,
and not to be outdone I silently pointed a finger at the absurd
legend *'pizzicàgnolo'* which happened to catch my eye. 'What's
it mean?' William demanded, and I was still considering my
reply when Geoffrey suddenly stopped dead in his tracks and
said excitedly, 'I say, Mr Wentworth. They never stamped us
in.'

'Stamped us in?' I retorted. 'Whatever do you mean, boy?'

'Our passports,' he said. 'You know. Nobody bonked them,'
and he banged a fist down into his open palm to show what he
meant.

'Nor they did,' William put in. 'Gosh, what a swizzle!'

'Well,' I said, laughing, 'what of it? I dare say as we are only
here for a couple of hours –'

'How should *they* know?' Geoffrey said. 'Besides, I *want* it
bonked.'

'There's no need to get in a state about it,' I said. 'And please talk sensibly.'

'So do I,' William shouted. 'I want it to say Italy. There's not much point otherwise.'

I was inclined to tell them both not to be silly little fools. If they thought I had brought them all this way simply to have their passports stamped they were no better than babies. But on reflection it did seem a little odd that we had somehow missed the frontier formalities, and of course there was the possibility that when we attempted to re-enter Switzerland there would be a fuss, since we should have nothing to show that we had ever left it or where we had been in the meantime.

'Very well,' I told them. 'If it is as important as all that we must see what we can do,' and I began to retrace my steps, with the idea of inquiring at the railway station. However, we soon spotted a policeman, or *carabiniere* as they say, and to save time I put our little difficulty to him. We had come, I explained, from Switzerland, just for the day, but through some oversight our passports had not been stamped on entry. Would he kindly advise me how to regularize the position?

'*Passaporto?*' he said.

'Yes,' I replied, speaking very slowly and clearly. 'Not stamped. *Sapristi?*'

It was soon clear that he understood little if any English, and having myself no great command of Italian I took my passport from my inside breast pocket and opened it at the page bearing the Swiss entry stamp at Zurich. 'See?' I said.

'*Si,*' he replied.

'Now then,' I went on, squaring my shoulders, 'here' – and I laid a finger on the entry stamp – 'is Switzerland. *Schweiz.* Yes?'

'*Si,*' he said. '*Svizzera.*'

'As you will,' I replied. 'But here,' jabbing my finger on the empty space below, 'no stamp! *Marka? Indorsimento?*'

He nodded his head several times, but I have spent too many years as a schoolmaster not to recognize a look of utter incomprehension when I see one and I therefore brought my clenched fist sharply down on the open passport. *'Bonk!'* I said, shaking my head to indicate that it had not been done.

'Try *bonka*,' one of the boys advised. 'They always put an "a" on it.'

The officer smiled vaguely, looking up and down the road as though for help, and I began again at the beginning. *'Schweiz,'* I said pointing. *'Svizzera.* Yes?'

*'Svizzera,'* he said. *'Si.'*

'Good!' I said. *'Buona!* But Italy – *Italia* – no!'

*'Italia,'* he agreed, 'no!'

'Well then!' I cried in exasperation. But it was useless. The policeman, with a polite *'Scusa!'* took my passport from me, flipped over the pages, studied my entry visa for America for a moment, and handed it back with a bow. 'Come!' he said, finally.

We followed him, willy-nilly, for a few hundred yards until we came to what I surmised, rightly, to be a police station, where to my great satisfaction I very soon found myself talking to an officer who spoke, on the whole, very good English.

'But Mr Wentworth,' he said, raising his eyes from my passport, when I had briefly explained the situation, 'Lugano is in Switzerland. There is no need for your passport to be stamped until you cross the frontier.'

'Then we are not in Italy?' I cried, unable to believe my ears. 'God bless my soul! But everybody speaks – the signs – I always thought the St Gotthard...'

'We also speak German in Switzerland, as you know, and we are not, I am happy – we are not, that is to say, in Germany. We speak French, in the Valais, and we are not in France. Yes?'

'You also speak excellent English,' I said warmly, 'and you are not –'

'Exactly,' he said. 'Though that is rather different.'

I cannot think, looking back, how I came to make so stupid a mistake. But there it was, and I could only be thankful that the two boys remained out of earshot during our conversation. All the same, I was not out of the wood by a long chalk.

'My two young charges will be sadly disappointed,' I told

the official, after apologizing for so unwarrantably wasting his time. 'They had set their hearts, for some reason, on having Italy stamped in their passports.'

'So?' he said, smiling. 'It is always the same, when we are young. But it is only a few kilometres to the frontier, on the Menaggio road. Would it not be possible – ?'

I glanced at my watch. 'Unfortunately,' I said, 'we have to catch a train back to Switzerland – to Brunnen, that is to say – at half-past three. And we have not yet lunched. These formalities, in my experience, take time.'

'I see,' he said. 'Yes. One moment, monsieur.' He left me to confer briefly with one of his colleagues, and returned with an expression of the greatest delight. 'All is arranged,' he said. 'Please to follow me.'

Well, to cut a long story short, the good-natured fellow took the three of us out to the frontier post and back. In a police car! 'Gosh, we're doing eighty!' young William shouted, and so we were, though it was only in kilometres of course. 'You are really extremely kind,' I said to our friend, but he merely smiled and said, 'Leave everything to me,' which I was only too glad to do. We were stamped out of Switzerland and into Italy in the twinkling of an eye, and as we stepped from the farther post on to Italian soil I could not resist the temptation to raise my hat in the air and cry gaily, 'Well, boys, what do you think of that?'

'Whacko!' they both said. 'But it seems funny – '

'Time to be going, if you want any lunch,' I told them, and in a minute and a half, all told, with many friendly grins and shouts of 'Stay a bit longer next time', we were stamped out of Italy again, *'Bonk, bonk, bonk!'* as William aptly put it, describing our whirlwind progress. 'And one *bonk* to come,' his brother added, as we approached the Swiss frontier post once again.

Here, however, there was an unexpected hitch. Two customs men sternly demanded whether we had anything to declare – any silks, leather goods, watches, cameras, etc., and before I had time to say a word one of them made a dive for my waistcoat pocket and dragged out my gold half-hunter. 'Italian, no?' he said. 'You bought her in Milan just now?'

'That watch belonged to my great-grandfather, young man,' I replied with some heat, 'and what is more – ' But I suddenly noticed that everyone was laughing, including our policeman friend, and there was nothing for it but to join in. What a people, eh?

So there it was. The four of us lunched together, at my expense (or rather at my employer, Mr Bennett's, strictly speaking, though I am sure he would have been the first to authorize the extra expenditure, had he been with us), and a very jolly meal we made of it. 'Any time you are passing through Fenport, Hampshire,' I said to our good friend when the time came for us to part, 'don't fail to look me up'; and he promised that he would, or wouldn't, rather. 'I really mean that,' I added. And so I did.

'The funny thing *is*,' William said sleepily as our train climbed up towards Airolo, 'how when we were in Italy already we had to sort of go out of Switzerland to get into it again. Into Italy, I mean. And then we went out of Italy and into Switzerland, so as far as I can see we ought to be in Switzerland *now*.'

'So we are, William,' I said.

'But in that case – '

'Oh, stow it, Bill!' his brother said, and though I do not in the ordinary way allow rudeness to pass unchecked, even between close relations, I left it at that.

# Scotched Rumour

It is good to be back in one's own country again, with solid, sensible words like 'Family Butcher' in the shop windows instead of that absurd *pizzicàgnolo* (which means 'pork butcher', I am told) and policemen in proper helmets. One misses the mountains, of course, and the air, which has been likened, I forget by whom, to champagne. But I feel very fit after the holiday, and the two boys benefited I am sure both mentally and physically. 'They tell me they never had a dull moment in your company,' Mr Bennett very kindly wrote when sending a final cheque which will be more than useful. 'I only wish I could have been with you to share the fun.' Speaking for myself I am thankful that he was not, since I should not have been there had he been able to accompany us. But no doubt he meant it kindly.

Having no further engagements at present I am settling down into the old routine at Fenport, and have no intention yet awhile of renewing my advertisement for temporary employment in *The Times*. One needs a little rest at my age, greatly though I have enjoyed my varied experiences. My three weeks in the heart of Wiltshire, followed by this fortnight abroad, have amply repaid the trifling original outlay, both in money and health. I could eat a horse, as they say.

The second-hand furniture nuisance has died down, I am thankful to say. None too soon, for really it was very difficult to know how to get rid of all the people who brought odds and ends for me to see, and my little cottage is seriously over-crowded. I suppose it was weak of me to buy an egg-collector's cabinet, for I am no oölogist, but at eight and sixpence it was something of a bargain and may well come in handy in the long run. I have a plan for removing the partitions and filing receipts and so on in the drawers. Or I may present it to Burgrove, if the Headmaster approves. We shall see.

Meanwhile the most ridiculous rumours are going about here. My own concerns are no business of anyone else's, and I could see no necessity to tell people here that I was seeking temporary employment, but my absences have been noticed, of course, and the gossips have been busy. 'I hear you were caught trying to smuggle second-hand watches out of Italy,' Mrs Wheeler astonished me by saying, in the full hearing of the tobacconist. 'Was it in aid of this antique business of yours in Wiltshire – or Northumberland, is it?' What a farrago of nonsense! It was all I could do to keep my temper.

'Really, Mrs Wheeler!' I exclaimed. 'I did not think that you, of all people, would listen to such silly talk. If Miss Stephens has been going about – '

'Oh, Mr Wentworth!' I was dismayed to hear Miss Stephens herself exclaim. 'How could you?' She must have followed me into the shop without my noticing, and I had no option but to apologize.

'I am sorry if I appear to have been talking about you behind your back, Miss Stephens,' I said stiffly. 'But upon my soul, the tittle-tattle that goes on in this place is enough – '

'There's so little else to do, you see,' Miss Stephens said. 'We can't all go dashing off to the Continent on mysterious errands. You shouldn't be such a dark horse, Mr Wentworth.'

'Dark horse, indeed!' I began, fingering my tie. 'It is true that I have been in Switzerland for a short spell – '

'Well, I'm glad you don't deny *that*,' Miss Stephens said. 'Or I should have to confound you by producing Myra Fitch's letter.'

'Mrs Fitch!' I cried, colouring despite myself. 'Well, well, well. Good gracious me!'

'She is an old friend of my mother's,' Miss Stephens said, 'and Mother sent on her letter about her holiday. She thought it might interest me, as it said quite a lot about a man from Fenport. It did.'

'Aha!' put in Mrs Wheeler, to my great annoyance. Mrs

Fitch is a very charming lady, who was good enough to help
me look after the boys on one or two of our expeditions in the
mountains, and naturally we spent my last evening together on
the hotel terrace, admiring the tranquil waters of the lake and
talking over this and that, as one does. Had I been ten years
younger, I dare say – who knows? – I might have suggested a
stroll along the shore, but the night air grows a little chilly after
dinner. But it is no business of anybody's that I can see.

'An ounce of Richmond Curly Cut, please, Mr Gooch,' I
said loudly, to show the two ladies that I had no wish to
continue the conversation, which seemed to me quite unsuit-
able for a tobacconist's shop. 'And a box of matches.' But it
takes more than a box of matches, however briskly ordered, to
persuade Miss Stephens to leave well alone.

'I can give you her address, if you like,' she told me, with an
archness that I found most distasteful.

'I have it, thank you,' I replied, before I could stop myself,
and raising my homburg with as much politeness as I could
muster bade them both good morning. The whole affair is
trifling, but it is difficult to get it out of one's mind. One cannot
help wondering, naturally, what Mrs Fitch said in her letter.
Nothing to my discredit, I'll wager.

So her name is Myra, eh?

To quieten the spate of talk I have thought it best to let it be
known in the district that I have recently taken one or two
temporary posts, to eke out. One would have preferred to keep
this sort of thing to oneself, but something had to be done to
scotch the rumour (started, I shall always believe, by Megrim)
that I had become a kind of Queen's Messenger and was likely
to leave for Ankara at any moment. Another theory I heard
being discussed in the Post Office was that I had business
interests abroad – I wish I had – and that 'this second-hand
furniture racket', as one man had the impertinence to call it,
was only a blind. It was getting beyond a joke. Anyway the
truth is now out, and the result is that I am being bombarded
with surreptitious gifts of fruit and vegetables and so forth.
People are very kind, but really! I have a sufficiency of means,

as long as I am reasonably careful, and much as I have always enjoyed *Cranford* (one of my favourites since I was quite a young man) I do not at all relish the role of a Miss Matty, however well meant the thought behind it. They will be setting my cottage up as a sweet-shop next! It is hard to know what to do, without giving offence, and in any case one cannot return a cauliflower left, without message of any kind, in the tool-shed. Even when I caught Mrs Wheeler red-handed putting a dozen eggs down by the back door she managed to make a tremendous favour of it. I mean a favour to her, of course. 'I'm simply snowed under with the wretched things, Mr Wentworth,' she told me. 'So if you could *bear* to help me out . . .' I tried to pay for them, although I already had four dozen in the larder, but she said it was more than her life was worth under the Egg Marketing Scheme or some such extravagant rubbish.

I don't know, I'm sure. It occurred to me to make repayment in kind to some of these good people, and I did manage to leave a small gate-legged table in the Wheeler's garage and a pair of brass-bound bellows at Miss Stephens's place, besides one or two other bits and pieces which relieved the congestion in my sitting-room. But it was difficult work after dark, and little good came of the plan in the end. All the pieces were recognized and returned, either direct to me or via the people who had sold them to me while the second-hand furniture rumour was at its height, and the general belief (which I had not the heart to deny) was that the whole thing had been the work of a practical joker, who had raided my cottage and distributed my belongings at random. 'And a joke in damn bad taste, too,' Mr Wheeler remarked to me with a good deal of heat. One way and another there was quite a fuss, with everybody doing everything they could to make it up to me. It is all rather embarrassing, and I often wish I had some sympathetic soul, like Myra Fitch, to talk things over with.

I thought it only civil, in passing, to send her a card – or brief note, rather; nobody who knows the postmistress here would send a postcard even on quite ordinary topics, as was mine I need hardly say – to inquire about her journey home among other things, and she replied with a very kind letter, which filled my head with what might have been dangerous thoughts in a less balanced man. What have I to offer a lady after all, even if the thing were feasible, except a small pittance and an outhouse full of vegetables and corner cupboards? Ah well! There it is. I wrote a long reply, not wishing to seem unfriendly, and as luck would have it ran into Miss Stephens on my way to the post. 'Caught you, Mr Wentworth!' she cried gaily, eyeing the envelope in my hand with a great deal of curiosity. 'There are going to be some sad hearts in Fenport when the announcement appears in *The Times*.'

I might have made a sharp reply, had I not caught a glimpse of what looked suspiciously like tomatoes in her bicycle basket. All this kindness, awkward though it is in a way, is quite disarming.

'The only announcement you are likely to see in *The Times*, Miss Stephens,' I said with a smile, 'is that Mr Wentworth is no longer available for temporary employment in positions of trust as he is setting up a greengrocer's shop in Fenport.'

It was rather naughty of me, I suppose, but her confusion was delightful to see. 'Caught *you*, I may say, Miss Stephens!' I added. 'It is very, very kind of you all, but it must really stop. I am quite all right, you know – quite all right.'

'Well,' she said, after a little silence, fiddling with her handlebars, 'we happen to be rather fond of you in these parts, you see. Still, I'll tell them.'

'My dear young lady,' I began, but found it quite impossible to complete whatever it was I had been about to say.

'You aren't going away on any more of these jobs, I hope,' she said. 'Not for a bit, anyway.'

'No, no,' I assured her. 'No. I shall spend the next few months among all my good friends in Fenport.'

I was wrong, however. By the very next morning's post I received to my astonishment a letter from my old Headmaster, the Rev. Gregory Saunders, M.A., telling me that the school was in some difficulty owing to the sudden illness of Mr Thompson and asking whether I would consider tiding them over by returning to Burgrove for the last five weeks of term.

'You shall have your old IIIA mathematical set. Do come!' he wrote.

Well! It did not take me long to make up my mind, as may be imagined. Back to the fray on Monday, eh!

I felt quite boyish as I sat polishing up my mathematical instruments after tea. It will be like old times to feel a piece of chalk between one's fingers again.

# Back to Burgrove

It is grand to be back here again, if only 'to tide us over' as the Headmaster puts it. Well, I have tided them over a few difficulties in my time, and I dare say I can do so again. Of course it is not the same. One cannot expect to step back into one's old seat at the top of the Common Room tree on the strength of a few weeks' temporary work. Easy does it. 'Tact, Wentworth old boy!' I said to myself as I shaved this morning. 'Tact and diplomacy!' And be sure I shall need both. I had to hold myself in pretty tight directly after chapel when I was hanging up my gown in the old familiar cupboard. They've put in a new light-switch, I noticed: one of those pull-down things on the end of a long string, which always seems to me a bit – not suggestive exactly. Anyway I don't like them. But it wasn't that. It was a young fair-haired fellow, new since my time and takes French and History they tell me.

'I say,' he said, 'you must be Thompson's stand-in. That's Mr Rawlinson's peg, if you don't mind my telling you. He's a bit touchy, you know.'

Well!

It was on the tip of my tongue to inform this young hopeful that the peg in question happened to be mine, that I had used it for twenty-seven years (ever since the Lent Term 1933, when old Poole gave up, to be precise), and that if anybody was trespassing it was Rawlinson. But my sense of humour won the day and I thanked him instead, saying with an assumption of the utmost gravity, 'I am most grateful for the hint. You have saved me from an irreparable blunder.' I then took my tattered old gown off the peg and hung it up again, with mock humility, on the farthest peg of all, right in the corner where the rolled-up map of Europe before the Great War used to stand.

'That's mine,' the young fellow said.

Still, all the familiar smells are there, and I snuff them up like an old war-horse returning to the fray. The Headmaster, in particular, has been most kind and welcoming. 'It is like a breath of fresh air to have you back with us, A.J.,' he told me, to which I replied, jokingly (though to tell the truth I was very much moved), 'The School hasn't often been short of fresh air, surely, Headmaster?' – a reference to the central heating system, which was always going wrong in my time. But he missed the point, I think. He has grown rather fat in late middle age, and is no longer known to the boys as the Squid, so Rawlinson tells me. Apparently they call him the Atomic Pile, in their modern way, or 'Tommy' for short, though his real name is, of course, the Reverend Gregory Saunders, M.A.

I had quite a shock on entering Classroom 4 for my first period with my old mathematical Set IIIA. The lower part of the wall, a sensible dark green in the old days, has been painted primrose, of all colours, with a lighter shade above, on some cock-and-bull theory that boys work better in cheerful surroundings. Nonsense! Boys work best when they have got their heads down over their books, with a master in charge who knows how to keep a firm hand on the young rascals, not when they are staring at fancy plastic emulsions. I suppose it is all part and parcel of turning the place into an 'Inspected School', which happened as soon as my back was turned. We are to have a second visit from these gentlemen in a week or two, the Headmaster tells me, and much good may it do us, or them. It is difficult enough in all conscience to teach boys the Theorem of Pythagoras, without being distracted by some Government popinjay sitting in judgement on the teaching methods of a man old enough (though by no means inclined) to be his father.

However, what was in some ways an even greater shock awaited me with IIIA. One's first duty, naturally, is to list the boys' names. Not that they are not already listed in the markbook by one's predecessor, but it makes a start and helps one to get acquainted and so on.

'Call out your names, please, one by one,' I told them, 'beginning from the left of the front row.'

'Do you want them in the form order, sir?' somebody asked.

'Naturally,' I said. 'That is why I said beginning from the left.'

'The top boy sits on the right, sir.'

I was thunderstruck. Boys at Burgrove sit at their desks in the order of the previous week's mark-lists, and in all my experience it has been the rule that the top boy sits on the left, the next boy on his right, and so on down the rows, ending with the bottom boy (who has to wipe the board and do other small chores) at the extreme right of the back row. Any other arrangement leads, in my opinion, to nothing but confusion.

'In my classroom,' I said, 'the top boy sits on the left. Now will you please get yourselves sorted out in the proper order as quickly as possible. And *quietly*! This is a classroom, not an elephant-house.'

It is extraordinary what an amount of noise a dozen boys can make with their feet, but eventually, after I had given a pretty sharp look to a biggish dark boy whom I caught tweaking another boy's ear as he passed, they all settled down again, and I began to write their names in my book as they called them out.

'Henderson,' I repeated, 'Blake, Wrigley . . . With a "W"?' I asked, looking up at the third boy in the row.

'Yes, sir. As in Wrekin.'

To my astonishment it was the boy next to him who answered, that is to say the third boy from the *right* (there being seven desks in all in the front row, as I ought perhaps to have made clear), and I immediately demanded an explanation. 'Has Wrigley lost his tongue?' I asked sharply. 'Or why do you take it upon yourself to speak for him?'

'I *am* Wrigley,' the boy said, looking genuinely bewildered.

'I see,' I said. 'Wrigley, did you not hear me say that you were to sit in your form order *beginning from the left*. Can you not count up to three?'

Wrigley simply stood there, looking helplessly about him, until the boy on the extreme right, who turned out to be

Henderson, kindly put his oar in. 'I think I can explain it, sir,' he said. 'Wrigley thought you meant our left, not yours. We all did, sir. That's why I'm over here where I am now, instead of being where I was when I started, if you see what I mean, sir?'

It is most important that a master should be fair, as well as firm, and believing that there had been a genuine misunderstanding I said no more than 'Very well, Henderson. But understand this, all of you. When I say "left" in this classroom I mean *my* left and nobody else's. Is that clear?'

'What happens if you are speaking with your back to us?' somebody asked.

'Stand up the boy who said that,' I ordered, in the voice I use only when I mean to have no nonsense. A fair-haired boy with glasses, whose face seemed vaguely familiar, rose to his feet a good deal more slowly than he will learn to do when he knows me a little better. 'I only meant – ' he began.

'Your name?' I said sternly.

'Mason, sir.'

'Mason!' I repeated. 'Indeed! Mason, eh? Well, well, well, well. Good gracious me! I see. How old are you, Mason?'

'Eleven and a half, sir.'

There was a fair-haired boy called Mason here in the old pre-war days, with whom I crossed swords on one or two occasions. Not a bad-hearted chap, but a little too inclined to overstep the mark. Indeed at times he was downright insolent, which I am scarcely the man to tolerate. It would be odd, though not of course impossible, if I were now to have the doubtful pleasure of trying to cram the elements of algebra into his son's head.

'May I sit down now, sir?'

Some of the other boys laughed at this, and I very soon spotted the reason.

'You appear to be sitting down already, Mason,' I said. 'So I am afraid I fail to see the point of your question.'

'Oh, so I am sir. I must have done it without noticing. What I mean is, may I have your permission to sit down, sir?'

If I had not been quite certain before, this sort of tomfoolery was enough to convince me of the boy's identity. I was

anxious to have no unpleasantness at my very first period with
IIIA, but the sooner this youngster was put in his place the
better it would be for all of us.

'Mason,' I said slowly, 'I believe your father – All right, boy,
sit down now – your father was at this school, I believe, in the
late 1930's. Is that so?'

'Yes, he was, sir. He told me all about you.'

'Indeed!' I said. 'That must have been very interesting. And
did he tell you, among all the other things, that I was not a
good man –'

'Oh, no, sir.'

'Not a good man,' I continued, raising my voice, 'to try to
be funny with? Do you happen to remember that, Mason?'

The boy had the impertinence to pretend to be racking his
brains, until I brought him to his senses by rapping sharply on
my desk with a pair of compasses.

'I expect he did, sir,' he said hurriedly. 'Sir, is it true, sir,
that you once fell backwards into a kind of basket in the boot-
room?'

'Be quiet, all of you,' I cried. 'We are wasting far too much
time. Henderson, where had you got to with Mr Thompson
before he became ill?' I had forgotten, until the boy I was
addressing told me his name was Sibling, that the form was
still back to front owing to this misunderstanding about left
and right, and there was a further tiresome delay while they
all got themselves back into their original positions.

And even then, as Henderson reminded me, I had still to
take their names down before we could get started.

'Henderson, Blake, Wrigley with a "W",' I said briskly –
'those I have got. Next?'

There was no reply, and I had to repeat the order. But the
silence continued.

'Come along, come along, wake up!' I said. 'You, there –
what is your name?'

'Kingsley,' the fourth boy said, looking frightened, as well
he might. 'But I'm not really next, sir.'

'Then why are you sitting there, boy?' I thundered, beginning to lose patience. Upon my soul, I began to wish I had my

old IIIA lot back again, muddle-headed as many of them were.

'It's Potter who's next in the order really, sir,' Henderson explained. 'But he isn't here.'

'Why is Potter not here?'

'I don't know, sir. I think he had to go and see Matron.'

'See Matron and die,' somebody sang out. I suspected Mason, but in my profession one has to be on one's guard against prejudice. So I let it go, and went on with my list of names as though I had noticed nothing. Which was just as well, as it turned out; otherwise I might not have got to the last boy before the bell rang for the end of the period.

We must really get down to it tomorrow. Still, the hour was not entirely wasted. As every schoolmaster knows, it is of the first importance to get on terms with one's boys. Let them see what they are up against right from the start, and then – off with a bang!

# Getting the Feel of It

Boys always want to know what is the *use* of what one is trying to teach them. Thus they are always more ready to find out how much wallpaper is needed to decorate a room than, let us say, to factorize an expression or follow a theorem involving tangents. I suppose it is natural enough, in a way, and I do my best to point out some of the applications of mathematical laws and principles to modern life. But one has to be on one's guard against being led astray into time-wasting digressions. One tip, that may be helpful to young men just starting out on the long furrow, is to watch your step when the boys begin to lean back and cross their legs. It means that the young rascals are counting on a good ten minutes' break from real work, and is one of the danger-signals that should never be disregarded. I make it a rule to get straight back to $x$ and $y$ as soon as I see it.

This morning's discussion with IIIA about the diameter of the sun (it originated, rather oddly, in a problem we were working on together about the price of eggs) went on perhaps a little longer than I generally permit, but that was because some valuable lessons seemed to me to emerge in the course of it. The importance of angular measurements, for one.

'Was there ever a time, sir,' Wrigley asked, while I was writing some solar dimensions on the board (and finding incidentally that chalk still breaks on the down stroke just as it always did), 'when people thought the sun was no bigger than the earth?'

I could not resist telling them of some of the weird misconceptions of the ancients, and in particular of a remark made by the Greek philosopher Epicurus which has always amused me, namely that 'the sun is about as large as it looks, or perhaps a little smaller'. This made them all laugh, with the exception of young Notting, rather a serious-minded boy for his age.

'Well, isn't it?' he asked.

He seemed genuinely puzzled, so I told the others to be quiet.

'What I mean, sir,' Notting went on, 'if it looked bigger than it does it *would* be bigger, wouldn't it, and if it were smaller than it is it would *look* smaller, so it must be as big as it looks.'

It is not always easy to follow the mental processes of young boys, so I took a turn about the classroom to clear my mind, confiscating a mint humbug from Mason as I passed his desk.

'And how big does it look to you, Notting?' I asked at length.

'Well, I suppose actually,' he replied, holding up a fore-finger and thumb, 'about that.'

'Exactly,' I said with a smile. 'About an inch across. And now what about *my* diameter? No, no – that will do, Mason – how big do *I* look? Measure the width of my shoulders in the same way, with your fingers. So!

'You had better do the same, all of you,' I went on, when Notting had satisfied himself that his mathematics master was three times as big as the sun. 'Extend your arms and make a note of my breadth as it appears from where you are sitting. Then we shall soon learn something about the relationship between distance and angular measurement.'

They at once complied, and I was about to warn them to take the measurement with thumb and forefinger, as Notting had done, and not between their first and second fingers, when the Headmaster looked in to ask some questions about cod-liver oil and malt, which I should have thought could have waited till break. He raised his eyebrows on entering, frowned at the boys, and was somewhat curt in his manner when put-ting his trivial query. There are times when I have scant patience with these headmasterly moods. He should take more exercise, in my opinion.

I was proceeding, after his departure, to demonstrate on the board from figures supplied by the boys how the width of an object can be determined by the apparent width of its extremities at known ocular distances (though I put it more simply, of course) when I became aware of a faint hum, or buzz, tending to increase momentarily in volume.

'Who is humming under his breath?' I demanded, swinging round on my heel.

Nobody owned up, though the humming continued, and I confess I derived a certain grim enjoyment from the thought that this old dodge should be tried out on an experienced hand like myself. It is almost impossible to pin down the actual culprit – culprits, rather, since more and more boys join in if the thing is allowed to continue. The lips do not move, and the utter immobility of the boys often has an unnerving effect on young masters. I remember a young Cantab, Griffiths was it? Or Fenner? Some name of the sort – anyway he did not last long – who reached the point of imagining that the noise was inside his own head and actually took pills for it, until Gilbert took him aside in the Common Room. Still, that was all a long time ago.

'There will be a serious row,' I told them, 'unless this humming stops immediately.'

Looking at their bland, expressionless faces (though one or two of the older ones attempted a puzzled wrinkling of the brows that might have fooled me thirty years ago) I was irresistibly reminded of my old IIIA of pre-war days, and very near burst out laughing despite my annoyance. 'You have had your last warning,' I said.

'I think it must be an aeroplane, sir,' Mason said.

'No doubt,' I said. 'Could it be the same one your father heard in similar circumstances, perhaps?'

A boy called Barstow in the back row had the impertinence to call out, 'It's coming nearer!' and somebody said he thought it was a Gipsy Major, or some such nonsense, by the sound of the engine.

'Very well!' I cried, bringing my fist down with a crash on my desk. 'Since it is impossible to work while this noise continues, we shall all have to make up the time lost after school hours this afternoon.' And to ram the warning home I ostentatiously took the time by my watch.

Instantly, as I had expected, the humming ceased.

'He's crashed,' Mason said — a remark that he may yet regret, when I have made up my mind what to do about it. For the moment my main concern was to waste no more time and get down to some solid work straight away.

'Open your books at Exercise 37,' I told them brusquely, 'and get to work on the first six examples. No, Hopgood, you may not. Wait till the bell goes, boy. If there are any difficulties — Well, Blake, what is it?'

'It's the aeroplane, sir.'

For the life of me I could not help following his pointing finger and there, sure enough, was a plane of some kind. However, it was only a second or two before I recovered my poise.

'I see,' I said. 'How curious that we should hear its noise so long before it arrived, Blake.'

'It's the speed of it, sir. The waves get left behind or something.'

'I know all about supersonic effects, thank you,' I said sternly. 'The only difficulty about your ingenious theory is that the sound arrives afterwards, not before.'

'This must be a subsonic plane, sir,' somebody put in. 'So it's the other way round.'

'Unless it's flying backwards,' Mason said.

The bell went just then, and saved one or two of them from what might well have been the surprise of their young lives. For the time being, at any rate. Later on, we shall see. I mentioned this aeroplane business to Gilbert during break, thinking it would amuse him to hear how badly this new generation of boys had mistaken their man. He tells me that the plane flies over regularly at about 10.30 every weekday morning and his guess is that the boys take advantage of it, but misjudged the timing on this occasion. Well, well, well! It begins to look as if this man Thompson, whose place I am temporarily filling, were an indifferent disciplinarian, who has allowed the Set to get a little out of hand. It may be necessary to tighten things up for a day or two, until they learn where they stand.

Hopgood, it appears, is no relation of the Hopgood II whom I so unfortunately stunned with a *Hall and Knight* back in 1939. This is a relief, really, as I have no wish to have that absurdly exaggerated affair dragged up again, should the boy's parents happen to come down. Not that I have anything to be ashamed of or regret, except that the wrong boy was hit. It is just that the thing is over and done with, as I told Rawlinson pretty straight after luncheon, when the talk happened to turn on the sons of Old Boys. I was a bit put out already, to tell the truth, by an extraordinary remark of the Headmaster's a little earlier. 'I assume,' he said, taking my arm, as we walked down Long Corridor together, 'I *hope*, Wentworth, that it was the Victory salute your boys were giving you this morning. But whatever it was, don't you feel it would be better – '

'We were discussing the diameter of the sun, Headmaster,' I interrupted with some impatience, 'and I really feel that in such matters my judgement is at least as good as that of a classical man. My methods of work, which are founded as you will agree on a great many years' experience – '

'Classical I admit to being,' he said. 'But even a man whose training has been mainly in the groves of Academe may perhaps claim some knowledge of the significance of gestures and the advisability or otherwise of their concerted use by boys during working hours. Or not, Wentworth?'

'Gestures!' I cried, with some heat. 'I know nothing of gestures. I happen to be more interested in the angle subtended by the sun – '

He did not, however, allow me to complete what I had to say.

'God bless my soul, A.J.,' he cried, slapping me with sudden friendliness on the shoulder. 'You have the power to astonish me, even now!'

Having no idea what he was driving at, I took myself off in something of a huff. Still, I think he means to be kind, and it is pleasant, taking one thing with another, to be back in the dear old place.

# A Brush with the Inspectors

It has been a tiring week, on the whole. No doubt Her Majesty's Inspectors have their work to do, and for all I know there may be schools that benefit from it, but I could wish that they would do it elsewhere than in my classroom when I am busy. It is a vexatious thing that this visitation should coincide with my brief stint of temporary work here at Burgrove, particularly as the Headmaster has allowed it to throw him completely out of his stride. Fuss, fuss, fuss! Really, for the best part of a week before these gentlemen were due one hardly knew whether one was on one's head or one's heels. Quite apart from all the sweeping and cleaning, which I dare say was overdue, the school piano has been moved five times to my knowledge and is now back in the music room where it started. I should have thought, as I remarked to Gilbert, that if these people want to see the school at work they should see us when we are fresh and at our best, not tired out with re-marking all the boys' hair-brushes in the downstairs washroom. Then, the usual issue of clean blotting-paper, which has always been on a Monday for as long as I can remember, was held back for three days, despite my protests ('They'll hardly give us many marks for industry,' I pointed out, 'if everybody's blotting-paper is as white as driven snow on a *Thursday*,' but nobody would listen to reason), and to cap it all I got wind of a plan to reorganize my own time-table without consulting me.

Of course I went straight to the Headmaster.

'I am told,' I began without preamble, 'that I am not to be permitted to take IIIA in geometry on Thursday morning, but that for some reason I fail to understand they will go to Gilbert for General Knowledge at that time. In all my long experience – '

'Certain rearrangements have had to be made as you know, Wentworth,' the Headmaster said, 'in view of the Inspection on Thursday and Friday – '

'That certain rearrangements *have* been made I know well enough,' I put in bitterly. 'Whether they have *had* to be made is another matter.'

'You will kindly leave that to my judgement,' he replied, in a tone I was inclined to resent. 'I have to consider what is best for the School. It is essential that the Inspectors' report should be a favourable one, particularly with regard to standards of discipline and methods of teaching.'

'Well?' I said, as he paused. 'I have yet to learn what all this has to do with the reorganization, without my knowledge, of my normal Thursday time-table, or,' I added (for I am a great believer in striking while the iron is hot), 'with the appearance in my classroom this morning of a new check duster, which will not rub out, in place of the old yellow one which will.'

The Headmaster sank into his chair with a weary sigh, confirming my growing suspicion that he is no longer really up to it and should begin to think of handing over to a younger man. 'I had supposed,' he said at length, 'that you would be glad to be spared the worry of having to teach with an Inspector in the room. However, if you insist on making an – if you prefer to be inspected, so be it. So be it, Wentworth. Only, for goodness' sake, don't come bothering me about dusters at a time like this, there's a good chap.'

I had half a mind to tell him that if he had not bothered about dusters in the first place I should have had no occasion to mention the matter. But he looked overstrained and in no condition to argue sensibly. Besides I had gained my main point. So with a quiet 'Worry? About an Inspector in my room? I'll soon settle *his* hash, if I'm not greatly mistaken,' I went off to see about the school roller, which had to be moved behind the cricket pavilion for some inexplicable reason. Upon my word, there could scarcely be more of a to-do if we were getting ready for Parents' Day.

As a matter of fact a very unsightly bare patch was left in the grass beside the gymnasium when we had moved the roller, and I was at my wits' end to find something to cover it up until Gilbert suggested moving the roller back there again. 'It ought to be just about the right size,' he said with a grin, and though I suppose I ought strictly to have referred the point to the Headmaster it seemed simpler to act on my own initiative. After all, if the decision was delayed for any length of time there would soon be a bare patch behind the pavilion and we should then be between the devil and the deep sea, as the saying goes. So I called up my helpers again, and as luck would have it ran into the Headmaster as we were trundling the thing back to the gym again. 'Good, good!' he called out. 'That's the spirit!' Which only goes to show. As far as I can see there is no coherent plan at all. So long as everything is being moved from one place to another and back again we are doing all we can to prepare for the inspection. It reminds me of the Army, in a way.

'Required to prove,' I announced, throwing a piece of chalk light-heartedly into the air and catching it again before it struck the floor, 'that the exterior angle of a triangle is equal to the sum of the two interior opposite angles. Yes, Potter?'

I had decided to run over the familiar theorem again, not for the benefit of Mr Edwards of Her Majesty's Inspectorate who was sitting at the back but because it is only by constant reiteration that one can implant the basic principles of geometry in young minds.

'I don't see how a triangle can have an exterior angle, sir,' Potter said. 'I thought the whole point of a triangle was that all its angles were inside.'

In the ordinary way I should probably have told young Potter to wait until I had set the whole theorem out on the board before raising difficulties, but this morning one had to make allowances. I had, as a matter of fact, in a short talk the day before, warned them all not to be afraid to ask questions just because a stranger was present, as it would have given an entirely wrong impression of a lively and not unintelligent Set if they had all sat silent and mumchance throughout. So that Potter was only trying, according to his lights, to carry out my instructions.

'It is true, Potter,' I explained, tossing the chalk up again, 'that a triangle is, by definition, a plane figure bounded by three straight lines – never mind that now, thank you, Henderson; I have another piece – and in that sense may be said to have interior angles only. But if, in the triangle ABC which I am drawing here, I produce BC to any point D, will you not agree that I have made an angle ACD which may fairly be called an exterior angle?'

'I suppose so, yes, sir,' Potter agreed, in that grudging way so typical of boys.

'But it isn't a triangle any longer,' Mason objected. 'It's more of a corner-flag lying on its side.'

I joined in the laughter – which I dare say surprised the Inspector, who is probably more used to the sort of class where boys have to be kept continually on a tight rein for fear of indiscipline. It would do him no harm to see that a friendly relaxed atmosphere is by no means impossible, if the master knows what he is about.

'You remind me of your father, Mason,' I observed jokingly. 'He, if I remember rightly, disapproved of a triangle with squares on each of its three sides, on the grounds that it looked more like three squares joined together with a space in the middle.' I could not resist stealing another glance at Mr Edwards as I said this, to see how he was taking the intimation (not altogether unplanned, I fear) that he was sitting in judgement on a man old enough to be teaching a second generation. But he was looking out of the window with an abstracted air, and it was all I could do not to ask him to be good enough to pay attention.

'In any case, Mason,' I went on, 'if you dislike my producing BC to any point D –'

'To *any* point D, sir?'

'Yes.'

'I see, sir.'

' – to any point D, you will be even more distressed by my next step, which is to draw CE parallel to BA – so.'

One gets a little out of practice, in retirement, at the difficult art of drawing on the board, and I snatched up the duster with the idea of re-drawing CE more nearly parallel to BA, only to find that I had hold of this wretched new check affair, full of dressing, which did nothing more than make an ugly smear in the middle of my diagram.

'Botheration!' I cried, as I think anybody might in the circumstances. 'Where is my old yellow rag?' And I threw the offending article aside on to my desk where, by cruel mischance, it knocked over a vase of daffodils, which had no business to be there in any case. If I had noticed them before I should certainly have had them removed out of harm's way, but one cannot have eyes in the back of one's head when concentrating on teaching.

'Who put those things there?' I demanded, and as nobody answered I put the onus on the top boy. 'Henderson,' I asked firmly, 'do you know anything about this?'

'No, sir,' he said. 'At least – I think there are flowers on all the masters' desks this morning, sir.'

'What in the name of goodness,' I began – but happening to catch Mr Edwards's eye I decided, out of loyalty to the Headmaster, not to complete the sentence. 'I see,' I said. 'Yes, yes. Of course. I was forgetting it was Thursday!' Which was rather a neat way, I flatter myself, of conveying to the Inspector the impression that it was quite the normal thing to have flowers in the classrooms on at least one day in the week.

'Are we going to have them every Thursday in future?' the little blockhead Wrigley asked, and though several of the boys immediately said 'Sh!' the harm was done. I must say, I blame the Headmaster chiefly, for trying to curry favour with these absurd fal-lals, and I only wish he had been present to see two of my boys attempting to mop up the mess with his infernal duster. 'It seems to be waterproof,' one of them rightly said, and in the end I had to send him out for a towel, which turned out to be not much better. 'I'm afraid it's brand new too, sir,' the boy complained. 'I don't know what's come over the place' – upon which I confess I could not for the life of me help exchanging a covert grin with the Inspector. What nonsense it all is, to be sure.

This little mishap unavoidably took up a good deal of time before I was ready to re-draw my parallel line CE, and I could not quite see what Mr Edwards was getting at when he took me aside later in the day and expressed his disappointment that in the fifty minutes he was with me I had not managed to reach the proof of the theorem I set out to explain.

'The proof?' I said. 'There is no great difficulty about that. Since the lines CE, AB are by construction parallel, the angle ACE is equal to the interior opposite angle BAC, and the exterior angle DCE – I have an envelope somewhere, I think – '

'Yes, yes,' he said. 'I am aware of the proof, Mr Wentworth. It was not myself I was thinking of but the boys.'

'Oh, the boys,' I said, laughing. 'Don't worry your head about the boys. They know it backwards by this time. Or if they don't they never will.'

'I see,' he said. 'In that case I find it a little difficult – perhaps you wouldn't mind telling me what you feel to be the basic principles of teaching young boys.'

'Basic principles!' I repeated, raising my eyebrows. 'There are no rules of thumb or short cuts to success in my profession, Mr Edwards. There is only one essential ingredient that I know of – a lifetime's experience.'

'Put *that* in your report,' I was tempted to add, 'and smoke it.' But I didn't, naturally. Nothing is to be gained by antagonizing that kind of person.

# End of Term

'Well, well, I suppose there can be no harm in it now.'

The boys had been pressing me to tell them something of the old days at the School – the 1930s seem like the beginning of the world to them, of course – and as it was the last lesson of term, when one traditionally relaxes a little, I had half a mind to indulge them. Mason was particularly anxious to know why the Headmaster used to be nicknamed 'the Squid' – a fact that he learned from his father, I don't doubt – but I was certainly not prepared to go into that. I was never very clear about it myself, to tell the truth, unless it had something to do with the octopus's habit of concealing itself behind a cloud of ink. Certainly, Mr Saunders used to put up an unconscionable number of notices on the board in his earlier days, mainly about bootlaces and the wearing of caps on school walks and similar trivia. But then again, I don't know. These things just happen, as often as not.

'I was only wondering,' Mason said, when he saw my frown. 'Of course, if it was anything you wouldn't like to – '

'That is not the point, Mason,' I said. 'One does not discuss the Headmaster in the classroom, as you very well know.'

'Like sex and religion,' somebody whispered: an impertinence that I should have come down on like a ton of bricks had it been a normal working period. I am not easily shocked, but some of these youngsters nowadays seem to me altogether too old for their years.

'The School was a very different place when I first came here as a young man,' I went on smoothly, hitching up my gown, 'and by no means so bright and comfortable as it is now.' And I told them, after cautioning two boys for whistling, how there was no linoleum in the upstairs passages and only six basins in the washroom for nearly seventy boys.

'There are only ten now,' Wrigley said.

'And a hundred and eight of us,' Blake added. 'If you count Hopgood, that is.'

'You shut up, Admiral,' Hopgood said, momentarily forgetting my rule that all remarks must be addressed to me. 'I wash a jolly sight more often than you do.'

'Where the carpentry shed now stands,' I continued, quelling these interruptions with a look, 'there was in the old days nothing but – What is the matter now, Mason?'

The boy was bowed over his desk in a half-crouching position and appeared to be engaged in some kind of a struggle.

'My tie's caught. In the hinge, sir.'

'Open your desk then and free it, boy,' I ordered. 'Though how in the world – '

'I can't, sir. The lid catches me under the chin.'

'Excuse me, sir, but your gown's hitched up.'

'I am aware of that, thank you, Potter,' I said coldly. 'Now, Mason, I give you exactly ten seconds to get that tie free and sit down properly, or there'll be serious trouble. Ten seconds, mind!'

'Can I do the count-down, sir?'

I took up a piece of chalk and flipped it into the air. 'We can easily spend the rest of the period on parallel lines, if you prefer it,' I warned them, taking a significant pace towards the blackboard.

'Oh, but, sir! Then we shall never meet,' some fool called out, and I should certainly have returned to normal teaching then and there if the rest of the Set had not promptly told the offender to be quiet and begged me to continue with my reminiscences.

'Please go on, sir. Sir, tell us about the old days.'

'Sir, there was a scimitar in the Museum . . .'

'Tell us about when you threw the hot-water jugs at Matron.'

'Sir, is it true you shot the Bishop of Saintsbury single-handed?'

'Oh, stow it, Coutts. I want to hear about the boot-basket.'

'Sir! Sir! My father said you were looking for your umbrella on a fine night . . .'

'That will do,' I said sharply. 'Quiet everyone, please. Wrigley, do I strike you as the kind of man who would throw water-jugs at anyone, Matron or anyone else?'

That silenced them, as I knew it would, and I took advantage of the pause to unhitch my gown and say a few straight words to the Set. 'Every school,' I told them quietly, 'has a lot of silly, exaggerated legends about the past, and it appears, I am sorry to say, that Burgrove is no exception. I make allowances for a certain amount of over-excitement on the last morning of work, but I have no intention of permitting my classroom to be turned into a bear-garden. If you cannot sit quietly and sensibly – Do you want to leave the room, Notting?'

'No, thank you, sir.'

'Then why is your hand up?'

'I wanted to know if I could ask a question, sir.'

'Very well,' I said patiently.

'Thank you, sir.'

The boy said no more. Indeed he casually picked up a pencil and began to doodle. So after staring at him for a minute or two in dead silence I rapped smartly on my desk. 'Get on with it, Notting,' I told him. 'We haven't got all day, you know.'

'Who? Me, sir?' the boy exclaimed, looking up with an innocent air which did not deceive me for an instant. 'I'm sorry, sir. I haven't got a question ready yet, actually. I only wanted to know if I could ask one in case I happened to think of one later, sir.'

'He wants to sort of bank one, I think, sir,' Mason was kind enough to put in, in his interfering way.

I thought I knew every dodge for wasting time that boys can get up to, but this was a new one even to me. However, I was more than equal to the occasion. If he wanted to cross swords with me he would soon find that two could play at that game.

'I see,' I said, without raising my voice. 'Very well, Notting. I am delighted to know that you believe in making provision

for the future. Perhaps, that being so, you will have the goodness to write out "I must not try to be funny in class" fifty
times – just in case I happen to want to set you an imposition
later, you know.'

The other boys roared with laughter, and I must say it was
all I could do to keep a straight face myself at Notting's comical
expression of discomfiture. Somebody called out 'Sucks to you,
Notty!', and though the expression is one I generally jump on
I let it go this time. It seemed to me to sum up the situation
rather neatly.

Needless to say there was no further trouble, and all the
boys listened attentively while I told them the true story of the
time the whole School went to the Tidworth Tattoo – or
*should* have gone to Tidworth, rather. The bell rang while I
was explaining how my own party were somehow misdirected
to Aldershot, so the dénouement will have to wait for another
time. If there is another time, of course.

'Well, Notting,' I said, as I rather sadly collected my books
for the last time. 'What do you think now of your question-
banking scheme?'

'Not much, sir,' he had the honesty to admit, and feeling
that he had learnt his lesson I let him off the fifty lines. After
all, end of term doesn't come every day.

> *Burgrove! Burgrove! Through the ages*
> *Boy and master sing your praise!*
> *Turn, yea, turn the crowded pages,*
> *Ne'er forget those happy days!*

How true it all is, I reflected as we sang the old song together
at End-of-Term Supper, though of course 'through the ages' is
stretching it a bit, as Gilbert says, for a school founded in 1907.
Still, there is such a thing as poetic licence, is there not? I for
one shall not forget 'those happy days', and tomorrow, when I
am alone with my own thoughts again in my little cottage at
Fenport, these last few snatched weeks at Burgrove will seem
like a dream, I dare say.

All the same, nothing is to be gained by indulging in
nostalgic self-pity, as though one were an old man with all

one's life behind one, especially as the Headmaster has just told me that it looks very much as if Thompson would be away for several months yet, so that, should I care to consider it . . . ! I shall certainly turn the matter over in my mind and let him know in a day or two. Temporary assistance, as the Headmaster pointed out (he does not scruple, bless his heart, to use every possible means of persuasion to get me back), is devilish hard to come by these days. 'I wouldn't dream of asking you, if I knew where else to turn,' he said to me; and though the sentiment was clumsily put I knew very well that he was thinking only of the sacrifice of well-earned leisure that my acceptance would entail.

In any case I am not likely to be dull during the holidays. As a Vice-President of the Football Club there will be this and that to do, no doubt. Then, of course, if I decide to come back here, I really must brush up my algebra a bit, which has become surprisingly rusty with disuse. I was very near floored the other day by a problem about the average speed of two cyclists, of all things! And I should not be very surprised if Miss Stephens is after me again about her precious Dramatic Society. Life is very far from being over! In fact it seems to be richer and fuller, in many ways, since my so-called 'retirement'. What with Switzerland and the Ripleys and one thing and another, not to mention Inspection Week here (though I am quite prepared to forget *those* particular 'happy days', School Song or no School Song!), one has been in quite a whirl.

· Talking of Miss Stephens, incidentally, I gather from Mrs Fitch (a lady whom I met in Brunnen, as I may have mentioned), that she (Myra Fitch, that is) hopes to come down to Fenport shortly with her old friend Mrs Stephens (who is Miss Stephens's mother, naturally) to stay with her. To stay with Miss Stephens, I mean. Anyway, she (Mrs Fitch) tells me in her last letter that she is very excited at the thought of seeing me once more.

It seems a strange coincidence that we should meet again. One can hardly suppose – And yet, I don't know. We shall see. There are times when I scarcely know what to think. In certain eventualities it might even be that my decision whether or not to return to Burgrove would ultimately depend on – well, on circumstances. At my age one is not a callow youth. Nor is one a doddering old man, with one foot in the grave, if it comes to that.

So there it is. Or may be, rather. Back to Burgrove for one more term, or – an engagement of an altogether less temporary kind? I don't know, I'm sure. Even supposing. But it is nice to feel that one may yet be of some use, in one way or another.